THE INNER METAGALAXY

THE INNER METAGALAXY

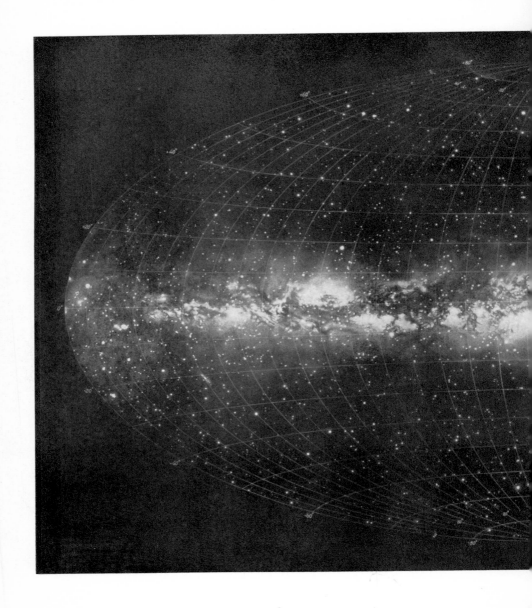

LONDON: OXFORD UNIVERSITY PRESS

BY HARLOW SHAPLEY

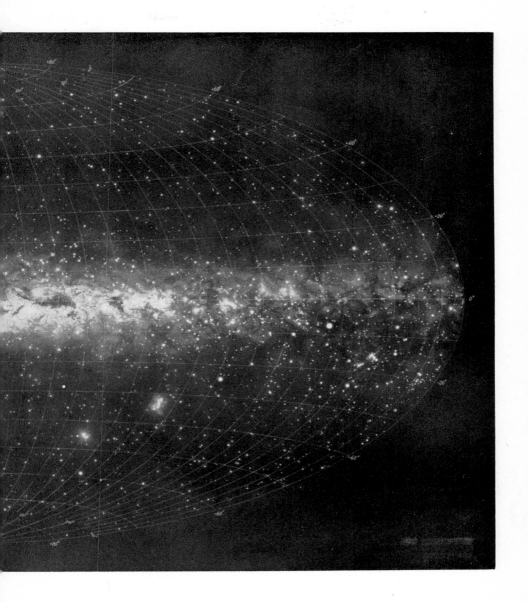

NEW HAVEN: *Yale University Press,* 1957

FRONTISPIECE: The Lund Observatory picture of the sky, showing the Milky Way and all stars to the 8th magnitude

Library of Congress catalog card number: 57-6877

PREFACE

This book had its inception as the Henry Norris Russell Lecture, delivered at a meeting of the American Astronomical Society in 1950. At that time the report on the progress of research on the Inner Metagalaxy opened so many lines of inquiry that attention was turned repeatedly from the completion of this general summary to the finishing of subsidiary investigations, such as the distribution of galaxies along the borders of the southern Milky Way, the extent of the galactic system in the anti-center direction, and a dozen interesting researches on the Magellanic Clouds. But a treatise recounting research in a live field never really gets finished. It is brought to a head at an arbitrary point through some agency, and this time the agent was the Sigma Xi Lecture Series at Yale University in March 1955, supplemented by a request from the editor that my lecture, "The Clouds of Magellan—A Gateway to the Sidereal Universe," be published in the *American Scientist*.

At the time the Russell Lecture was prepared, the Carnegie Astrograph at the Lick Observatory had but recently started on its important career of galaxy surveying, and the Schmidt telescope on Palomar had not made its famous Atlas of the northern sky. The making of a large-scale census of faint galaxies, after Hubble's sampling surveys of twenty years ago, had been almost wholly a Harvard Observatory operation. For that reason this volume largely concerns the scores of investigations undertaken by many workers at Harvard's Boyden, Agassiz (Oak Ridge), and Cambridge stations.

A few special investigations carried out at Harvard and elsewhere are but briefly mentioned in the present report; space limitations have dictated this procedure. For example, the galaxies as radio sources and the promising researches of Carpenter, Page, and Zwicky on associated galaxies, a field for the future, are not fully reported. Much of the early visual descriptive work, such as that of Bigourdan at Paris and Wirtz at Strassburg, is of small value in this age of photographic, spectrographic, and photoelectric instrumentation; it can be left aside at this time, along with reports on visual micrometric measures. On the other hand, I have occasionally repeated discussions of procedure and conclusions in order that the chapters may be more or less independent of each other. The internal behavior and structure of individual galaxies, except for certain details concerning our own and the Magellanic Clouds, are not considered an appropriate part of this account of the Metagalaxy.

My own work on galaxies and related subjects for the past thirty years has been much benefited from the observations, and discussions in print and in person, of many contemporary workers in the field, among them Wolf and Reinmuth at Heidelberg; Lundmark, Bernheimer, Holmberg, and their colleagues at Lund; Hubble, Humason, Smith, Baade, Stebbins and Whitford, Zwicky, Pettit, Sandage, and others in Pasadena; Curtis, Mayall, Shane, Wirtanen, and Kron at the Lick Observatory, as well as Carpenter, R. H. Baker, Page, Omer, Seyfert, Lindblad, Wyatt, Oort, Duncan, and Gamow among those not at the principal centers for galaxy research. But especially I am indebted to co-workers in the Harvard Observatory whose participation is gratefully acknowledged here and indicated specifically throughout the volume. In this final year Miss Jacqueline Sweeney has faithfully worked on details of observation, reductions, and the assembling of the raw material into a somewhat orderly volume. In the preparation of manuscript, figures, and diagrams for the printer Miss Catherine M. Hanley, Miss Ann B. Hearn, Pedro Kokaras, Mrs. W. H. Pinson, Miss Arville D. Walker, and Mrs. Shapley have had a hand.

A few words on definitions and nomenclature may be helpful. A galaxy needs defining as little as a star, but for the sake of clarity let us describe a galaxy as a *large* gravitational system of stars. In form it can be spheroidal, discoidal, spiral, mixed, or irregular; it can be in population dense or sparse; in distance relatively near or far; in apparent magnitude bright or faint, with a wide dispersion in total mass and intrinsic luminosity; but in linear dimensions it must be large. It is greater in size, and almost always in mass and luminosity, than the largest of the globular star clusters, such as Omega Centauri and Messier 13.

For a few of the galaxies special and somewhat misleading names have become established in the literature. The Andromeda "Nebula" is of course not a nebulosity but a great galaxy much like our own. The Sculptor and Fornax "clusters" are sparse spheroidal galaxies of

low total mass and luminosity which at first glance appear to be
ordinary open star clusters; they should properly be called superclusters. Providing some confusion, there is also a Fornax "cluster
of galaxies"—an assembly of twenty or more bright ones. The term
"star cloud" refers generally to the star and nebula aggregations along
our Milky Way—clouds that are small parts of our own spiral Galaxy.
But the Clouds of Magellan are nearby full-size galaxies.

The word "nebula" is now used almost exclusively for the dust
and gaseous nebulosities, in our Galaxy and in others, but we find
it convenient at times to use the adjective "nebular" when referring
to the faint hazy images of remote galaxies. The use of the term
"extragalactic nebula" as a synonym for the older and neater word
"galaxy" is gradually dying out. Finally, the terms "Metagalaxy" and
"metagalactic" refer to the total recognized assemblage of galaxies.
The Metagalaxy includes also whatever there may be in the way of
gas, particles, planets, stars, and star clusters in the spaces between
the galaxies. It is essentially the measurable material universe.

CONTENTS

CHAPTER 1. INTRODUCTION

In the course of our extragalactic explorations the time now seems appropriate to re-examine the distribution of galaxies in the neighborhood of our own, and to summarize what we have uncovered. The important contributions in this field from the western American observatories and from Sweden and Germany will of course be discussed, but more attention is given to the researches carried on at the stations of the Harvard Observatory. For nearly twenty years we have systematically recorded and measured the half million nearest galaxies. For the forty preceding years the accumulating Harvard photographs sampled the Inner Metagalaxy. More than a hundred articles and notes have been published on specific investigations of these cosmic units. The exploration of the neighborhood has involved studies of the numbers and distribution of galaxies in relation to distance and position in the sky. It has involved also the types and luminosities, galaxy clustering, and the average density of matter throughout intergalactic space.

One cogent reason for a comprehensive summary of the work on the Inner Metagalaxy at this time is that we have now essentially completed one epoch in metagalactic surveying and are opening a new one. The fast photographic emulsions and the wide-field, high-speed Schmidt type cameras which are now coming into general use should lead us soon into larger spaces and longer times; they should reach close to the 20th magnitude and to a billion years of light travel. Also the rapidly multiplying radio telescopes have entered the Metagalaxy effectively.

Another reason for the present examination is that such a large volume of space is now involved in our surveys to magnitude 17.5 and fainter that we can already discuss with confidence most of the outstanding features of metagalactic structure.

A. The astronomy of the outer world

In a sense our methods and results are rough. We have necessarily used provisional magnitude standards, unrefined classifications of galaxies, hesitant deductions of distances. It gives us some satisfaction, however, to be able to derive, from our awkward position near the edge of one dusty spiral, a fair picture of the whole universe of billions of galaxies. Of these billions, less than a dozen are within a million light years.

The Harvard surveys began as far back as 1898 when it was discovered that the long-exposure photographs made with the 24-inch Bruce camera at Arequipa, Peru, recorded thousands of new nebulosities. Later the photographic work at Heidelberg and the Mount Wilson and Lick sampling surveys with large reflectors, along with the resumption of a total sky-covering census of galaxies with the Harvard telescopes, began to establish the astronomy of the outer world. With photographic plates, spectroscopes, photoelectric photometers, color photography, and cosmogonic theory, we began to explore as deeply as possible into an expanding universe, eventually going beyond the neighborhood with which we are now concerned.

Our metagalactic neighborhood as here defined encompasses the majority of the galaxies (except the dwarfs) within a distance of 150 million light years. It is in a sense a local affair—local compared with the volume we know to be populated with galaxies. Doubtless we have already photographed at the Harvard, Lick, Mount Wilson, and Palomar observatories many superluminous galaxies at a distance of a billion light years.[1]

B. Photometric limitations

The surveys of galaxies discussed in this treatise are limited in general to nebular objects brighter than photographic magnitude 17.5. This limit is based on fairly reliable standards of stellar brightness. Fainter than that magnitude the stellar scale is not nearly so dependable as it must become before we can speak securely of the distribution of galaxies in remoter regions.

The deeper surveys of the future will probably be only sampling explorations, and for many problems sampling should suffice. Large-area surveys to the 20th magnitude, involving such detailed work as

1. In essentially clear space, as we assume space to be in the direction of the galactic poles, a galaxy of total absolute magnitude −18.5 (our tentative estimate for our own galactic system) would need to be only as faint as apparent magnitude 19.0 when a billion light years distant. It is probable that at least 1 per cent of the high-latitude galaxies with apparent magnitudes between 19 and 20 are at a distance of a billion or more light years.

we have undertaken for much of the Inner Metagalaxy, would be cumbersome and very costly. At the 20th photographic magnitude the galaxies are probably more than twenty times as numerous as at magnitude 17.5. The chief obstacle to dependable deeper surveys, or deeper sampling well distributed over the sky, will long be the insufficiency of good magnitude standards, stellar or nebular, between magnitudes 18 and 20. From the photographic work of Baade and others on a few northern Selected Areas, and from the photoelectric check-up by Stebbins, Whitford and Johnson, Baum and others, we already see the serious difficulty of establishing accurate sequences of faint magnitudes. We find such wide and nonsystematic divergences from the earlier published photographic values that not only do we foresee no simple straightening out of the existing magnitude scales for faint stars over the whole sky, but we realize also that cosmogonical deductions based on the numbers of galaxies per square degree at magnitude 19 and fainter are still provisional. Much observational work needs to be done before we can write out the final cosmography, or perhaps before we can closely approach it.

The magnitudes down to 17.5 in the Selected Areas (Kapteyn) and in the Harvard Standard Regions are relatively reliable, thanks to the decades of systematic photometric work at Groningen, Harvard, the Cape, and especially by Seares at Mount Wilson. Or if they are not yet wholly satisfactory, these all-sky-over standards can be rather easily rectified and smoothed with the help of the half dozen photoelectric photometers that are now used to some extent in basic photometry.

C. Instruments

At the Mount Wilson Observatory the 60-inch and 100-inch reflectors and at the Lick Observatory the Crossley 36-inch reflector have provided galaxy survey material. At Harvard, photographs made by a dozen telescopes have been involved in various phases of the surveys reported in the present monograph. Two identical patrol cameras have provided the material used for most of the magnitudes of bright galaxies. Their scale is 1 mm = 10 minutes of arc, and the galaxy images are therefore workably small. The series designated by the letters AM were made chiefly at Arequipa, but a few came from the South African station after the transfer of the telescopes in 1927 to

Bloemfontein. Plates of the AC series, made in Cambridge, form the basis for the magnitude work on bright northern galaxies. These two patrol cameras are equipped with 1.5-inch Cooke lenses of 13 inches' focal length.

The deeper surveys of the general metagalactic field in the south were made with the 24-inch Bruce doublet, most of them after its transfer from Peru to South Africa. The scale is 1 mm = 1′. This large camera uses plates 14 x 17 inches in dimensions, but only the central two-thirds of a plate can be dependably used for locating galaxies and for their measurement. Nearly 60 per cent of the sky was covered from the southern station. The Bruce camera has photographed over half a million galaxies. Some plates in high latitude show several thousand; others, in low latitude, none at all.

The northern galaxies were photographed on 8 x 10 plates made with the Metcalf 16-inch doublet at the Agassiz Station at Oak Ridge. It provides workable images of stars and galaxies over a central area of 25 square degrees. The scale is 0.6 mm = 1′. The plates, curved by air pressure to fit the focal field during exposure, require no distance correction over the area utilized in our studies.

Exposures with both of these larger cameras, on Cramer Hi-Speed or Eastman 103a-0 blue plates, were uniformly of three hours' length when used for the metagalactic surveys.[2] Such exposures, on the average, have reached magnitude 18.2 for the Bruce telescope and 17.9 for the Metcalf camera, with occasionally a much deeper reach when the emulsions were unusually fast.

The 60-inch reflector in South Africa, the 24-33-inch Jewett-Schmidt at the Agassiz Station, and various other telescopes and patrol cameras were occasionally and specially used for this work; but the systematic census is based almost entirely on the A (Bruce) and MC (Metcalf) plate series.

The marking and measuring of the galaxies, and of the stellar magnitude sequences, was carried out in Cambridge during the past twenty years by numerous participants, many of whom were authors or joint authors of the papers that present the results of the investigations. The plates from the southern hemisphere were made under the supervision of the late J. S. Paraskevopoulos, superintendent of the

2. Except in the "mopping up" after 1950, when the faster emulsions made it necessary to reduce exposures to two hours to avoid too heavy sky fog.

Figure 1. The Boyden Station of the Harvard College Observatory, Bloemfontein, South Africa

Figure 2. Messier 83, a bright southern spiral. Harvard photograph

Boyden Station. The plates of the Metcalf series, with few exceptions, were made by Henry A. Sawyer.

D. *The scope of this treatise*

Nearly all of the articles that report investigations of galaxies at Harvard have been published in the *Bulletins, Circulars,* and *Annals* of the Observatory, or communicated to the *Proceedings of the National Academy of Sciences* and included in the Harvard Reprint series. The volume on *Galaxies* [3] in the Harvard Books on Astronomy surveys nontechnically much of the work at Harvard and elsewhere prior to 1940. The most thoroughly studied of the individual galaxies have been, of course, the Clouds of Magellan. They have provided rich returns that have been presented in another forty articles by members of the Observatory staff. The two Clouds are described in some detail in Chapter 4 and they enter also into discussions of the local family of galaxies.

The present treatise will discuss:
the coverage of the metagalactic survey in eleven special areas;
the "13th magnitude" survey of the thousand brightest galaxies;
the Magellanic Clouds, the nearest of external systems, treated as a gateway to the outer universe;
characteristics of the Metagalaxy in the galactic polar zones;
dependence of distribution on galactic latitude;
the clustering tendency of galaxies, and the occurrence of cosmic density gradients in both the radial and transverse surveys;
the dust and gas of the southern Milky Way;
windows in the cosmic smog near the galactic plane;
the use of the cepheid-galaxy method of estimating galactic dimensions;
the direction of the galactic center and estimates of its distance;
the diameter of our Galaxy and the nature and extent of its enveloping corona;
the orientations of galaxies, their comparative dimensions, and the probable direction of their evolution.

A large segment of the Metagalaxy and a wide range of subject matter are covered. We cannot, however, from our explorations throughout a volume of space that is restricted to about 10^{25} cubic

3. Philadelphia, Blakiston, 1943.

light years, contribute usefully to questions bearing on the expansion of the universe [4] or on its radius and mass. Nor shall we consider in detail the inner structure of individual galaxies.

The first objectives of the surveys of the Inner Metagalaxy have been to get some idea of the average density of matter in metagalactic space and to search out structural patterns in the distribution of a few hundred thousand of the most accessible galaxies in order to throw some light on the past and future history of the material universe. Additional objectives concern the frequency of galaxy types, the spread in dimensions and luminosities of galaxies, and the dusty borders of our own Milky Way. We believe that to a limited extent we have successfully approached these goals.

4. For the important discussion of red-shift measures by M. L. Humason, N. U. Mayall, and A. R. Sandage, see *Ast. Jour., 61,* 97–162 (1956).

CHAPTER 2. THE COVERAGE AND CONTENT OF ELEVEN SURVEYS

Somewhat more than 25,000 square degrees of the sky, in galactic latitude higher than 20°, are open to effective extragalactic exploration. In lower latitudes we are blocked by dust and gas associated with our galactic system, and star crowding in some regions further confuses a total census. Of the open area, about 20,000 square degrees are substantially clear of light scattering and the resultant dimming which we commonly call space absorption.

A general dimming by two- or three-tenths of a magnitude in the high-latitude sky is possible, and for the present this amount is accepted, although such space absorption is not yet clearly demonstrated. The extraordinary blueness of distant spirals, recently recorded by Whitford,[1] argues against any high-latitude absorption, at least for many areas in the polar zones. The hypothetical increase in *general* absorption from the galactic poles down to latitudes ±30° is generally ignored in our analyses, and properly so in view of the natural irregularities in the distribution of galaxies.

Various surveys have shown that on the average we find one galaxy per square degree brighter than apparent magnitude [2] 15.2 in high galactic latitudes. If metagalactic space is on the average uniformly populated with galaxies, at least to the depth of about $10^{8.3}$ light years to which our census extends, the total number N of galaxies in high-latitude regions of the sky to magnitude m is of the order of

$$N = 2 \times 10^{4 + 0.6 \ (m - 15.2)}.$$

To magnitude 17.5, we should therefore find approximately half a million galaxies in latitudes greater than 30°, and perhaps an additional 150,000 should be found in partially obscured lower latitudes.

1. Albert E. Whitford, *Ast. Jour.*, *58*, 49 (1953); *59*, 194 (1954); and *Astroph. Jour.*, *120*, 599–602 (1954).

2. In this volume all magnitudes, unless otherwise indicated, are on the photographic (blue) scale.

Many of the plates of the Harvard metagalactic survey reach to galaxies fainter than the 18th magnitude. The total number of galaxies that have been photographed with the Bruce and Metcalf doublets accordingly is estimated at approximately a million. Of this number, about one-third have been identified and marked on the photographic plates, magnitudes have been estimated for approximately 170,000, and individual positions determined for 14,000.

Because of the abundance of galaxies, it has not been possible to investigate the population for the whole sky, even in our survey to magnitude 17.5. We have had to choose areas of special significance. The number of individual galaxies to magnitude 17.5 in the areas selected for detailed examination is approximately 175,000, or one-fourth of all that are brighter than that magnitude limit. In the areas selected another 160,000, fainter than 17.5, are on the plates and have been recorded. This total number of individual galaxies is of course much greater than that involved in earlier published surveys,[3] and certainly should suffice to give us a general idea of the distribution of galaxies throughout the inner metagalactic system. But the work has several shortcomings.

One difficulty in the study of the brightness of these faint galaxies lies in the aforementioned precarious magnitude standards, especially those of the southern sky. Another is the uncertainty involved in locating and measuring galaxies in low latitudes where the rich star fields and the Milky Way nebulosity disturb the galaxy counts and magnitude measures. A third handicap in the accurate interpretation of the distribution in our neighborhood lies in the wide spread of the intrinsic luminosities of galaxies—from absolute magnitude −19, or even somewhat brighter, to the dwarfs of magnitude −12 and fainter. This spread makes for a heavy preferential selection of high luminosities in surveys down to a given apparent magnitude.

A. Depth of the surveys

In clear space the giant galaxies with absolute magnitude $M = -18.5$ are included in our study if within a distance of 500 million light years. The intermediate galaxies, with luminosities like that of the Small

3. The current Lick Observatory census when fully published will involve counts of comparable numbers of galaxies, possibly considerably more.

Magellanic Cloud, are at a distance of 150 million light years when the apparent magnitude is 17.5. The extreme dwarfs, however, with absolute magnitudes of -12, appear in our surveys only when not more than 25 million light years distant.

We shall say that the eleven surveys extend out to about 150 million light years for average galaxies, with a good sampling of the giant and supergiant population out to half a million light years, and with general neglect of all but the nearest few thousand of the dwarf galaxies.[4] In view of the evidence presented later that spirality is a property chiefly of the more massive and luminous galaxies, we may assume that the spirals within 200 million light years are practically all included in our surveys. (Unfortunately, on the basis of photographic appearance alone we cannot as yet discriminate between dwarf and giant galaxies, except possibly for this spirality criterion. Velocity measurements, when available, can assist to some degree.)

B. Coverage

The distribution of the Harvard surveys of faint galaxies is shown in Table 1 and Figure 3. The right ascension and declination coordinates are used in this equal-area Aitoff projection, with some of the galactic latitude lines superimposed (β 0°, ±20°, ±60°). The figure does not show quite all of the regions we have worked on at the Harvard Observatory. Special surveys by Carl K. Seyfert[5] and the writer[6] are not included, nor is Region L along the southern Milky Way.

The larger surveys of faint galaxies, seven in number, and four smaller special surveys, are described separately in this chapter, with a preliminary comment on one or more of the results derived for each from the magnitudes, positions, types, and population distribution. The whole-sky census of the brightest galaxies (the 13th magnitude survey in *Harvard Annals, 88,* No. 2) is not referred to in Table 1, but it is described in the next chapter. In Chapters 5, 6, 7, 8, and 10 we present the seven larger surveys in much more detail than we give preliminarily in the following paragraphs.

4. Analogously, dwarf stars in our galactic system are relatively scarce in catalogues that are limited by apparent magnitude.

5. Carl K. Seyfert, *Harv. Ann. 105,* 219–36 (1937).

6. *Harv. Bul.,* No. 909, 1–3 (1938) and *Harv. Ann., 88,* No. 2 (1932).

Region A. The north celestial polar zone. In declinations higher than +70°, 16,639 galaxies have been identified and measured for distribution and brightness. The magnitudes are based on the North Polar Sequence. Fifty-six three-hour-exposure photographs taken at the Agassiz Station with the 16-inch Metcalf doublet (scale, 1 mm = 1.6 from the basis of the survey. They were supplemented by eleven plates made with the patrol camera to handle the brighter objects.

Table 1. Eleven Selected Surveys

Region	Area in Square Degrees	Approximate Number of Galaxies	Principal References *
A	North celestial polar zone	1,240	16,600	*Ann.*, 106, No. 1 (1938)
B	South celestial polar zone	2,760	36,000	*Ann.*, 105, No. 8 (1937) Reprint 140 (1937)
C	North galactic polar zone	2,760	95,000	Reprint 347 (1951)
D	South galactic polar zone	2,760	80,000	*Circ.*, No. 423 (1937) Reprints 145, 150, 154 (1938), 194 (1940)
E	Declination +43° belt	1,300	22,300	Reprint 208, 209 (1940)
F	Canopy	3,600	78,000	Reprint 333 (1950) *Ann.*, 88, No. 7 (1950)
G	VSF 233	320	2,100	*Circ.*, No. 411 (1936)
H	Horologium	174	7,900	*Ann.*, 88, No. 5 (1935) Reprint 115 (1935)
J	Fornax and Eridanus	175	2,100	*Ann.*, 88, No. 3 (1933) No. 6 (1937)
K	Coma and Virgo	100	2,780	*Ann.*, 88, No. 1 (1930)
L†	Southern Milky Way borders	8,000	50,000	Reprint 427 (1955)

* The publications are all in Harvard Observatory series.

† The number of galaxies is not corrected for overlapping plates (perhaps 10%). Region G and a part of Region B are included in Region L, which is not indicated in Fig. 3.

The irregular distribution of galaxies reflects in part the ubiquitous clustering tendency; but in the half of the field nearest the Milky Way the irregularities are clearly attributable to interstellar absorption and in large part to a flare of absorbing material extending out 30° from the Milky Way circle. The outstanding result of the survey is the

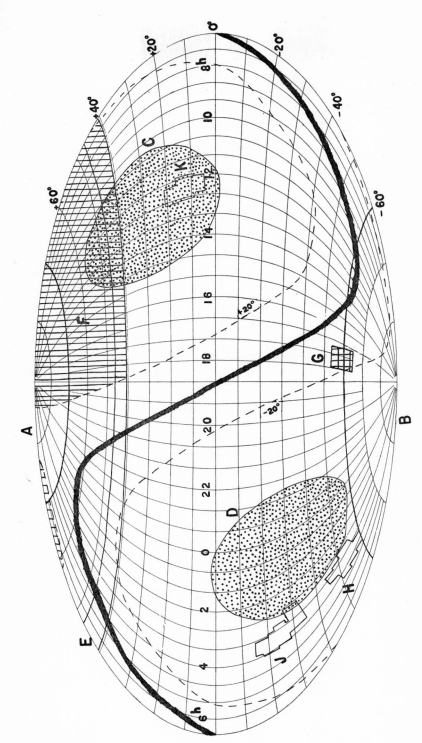

Figure 3. Location on an Aitoff projection of ten special surveys in the metagalactic census. Coordinates are declination and right ascension. The heavy curve is the projection of the galactic circle.

evidence that the North Polar magnitude standards are situated in a region of conspicuous obscuration which may amount to as much as half a magnitude. Counts of stars on small-scale plates for this region show the obscuring effect, but much less clearly than it is shown by the galaxy counts. Many of the stars are probably less distant than the obscuring nebulosity, and their magnitudes are therefore unaffected. (See Chapter 7.)

Region B. The south celestial polar zone. Eighty-seven Bruce photographs (scale 1 mm = 1′), each of three hours' exposure on Cramer Hi-Speed plates, cover the area from declination —60° to the South Pole. This survey is the least satisfactory of those completed at Harvard because of the necessity of working on fields at relatively low altitudes. The percentage of misidentifications in low latitudes is probably higher than usual.

The heavier absorption in low latitudes is shown in the plot of the distribution of 36,000 galaxies to magnitude 17.5 (Fig. 28). The average galaxy population over the whole zone is only twelve galaxies per square degree, indicating an absorption on the average of half a magnitude more than in high galactic latitudes—an expected result, since the galactic circle cuts through the edge of this zone.

It is noteworthy that the population of galaxies around the Small Magellanic Cloud (β —45°) is distinctly less than around the Large Cloud (β —33). The difference is presumably an indication not only of unusual absorption in median latitudes but also of intrinsic metagalactic unevenness. "The access to the Nubecula Minor on all sides is through a desert," stated Sir John Herschel. The Large Cloud appears to be at the southern end of an extensive cloud of galaxies extending from near the south galactic pole; and the Small Cloud appears to be in an area of subnormal population. Sample surveys with Schmidt telescopes to magnitude 19 should settle the question of the existence of relatively heavy absorption around the Small Cloud. (Chapters 4 and 7.)

The evidence for the occurrence of extensive clouds of galaxies first appeared in this survey of the region around the south celestial pole. Other clouds have now been recorded in various surveys.[7] The best

7. Walter E. Bernheimer, *"A Metagalactic Cloud between Perseus and Pegasus," Nature, 130,* 132 (1932). See also K. Lundmark and Walter E.

known, because of the brightness of its members, is the sparse extension far southward of the relatively nearby Virgo group. (Chapter 9, § B.)

Region C. The north galactic zone β +60° to +90°. The region around the north galactic pole is the most important part of the sky for the study of galaxies. Its position makes it available to all of the large telescopes and spectroscopes of the world. Heidelberg, Mount Wilson, Palomar, Lowell, Lick, Lund, Stockholm, and Harvard have all investigated its brighter population. In this area lies not only the highly useful Virgo Cloud of galaxies at a distance of about twenty million light years but also scores of more distant clusters of galaxies, including the frequently studied Coma cluster, one degree from the north galactic pole. There is little evidence of space absorption in this polar zone, at least to an extent that would appreciably affect determinations of the surface distribution of galaxies or of galactic stars lying in this direction.[8] An early probe in the Virgo region, which gave measured magnitudes, positions, and dimensions of 2,778 galaxies, is described below (Region K).

In the 2,760 square degrees with $\beta > 60°$ there are, according to our survey, 350 galaxies brighter than the 13th magnitude, thus making this easily the richest segment of the sky out to a distance of some twenty million light years. Even down to magnitude 17.5 the region has more than double the average richness of the sky above latitude ±30°. (The Virgo Cloud is of course partly responsible for the richness in fainter galaxies.)

Ninety-five thousand galaxies brighter than photographic magnitude 17.5 have been marked on the 126 long-exposure plates used for the study of this polar zone. The distribution is illustrated and discussed in Chapter 6. To magnitude 17.5 the average population in galaxies over the north galactic polar zone is 45.1 per square degree, which appears to be about 1.75 times the average population of the south galactic polar zone. This striking difference is the most important contribution from the high-latitude surveys. Refinement of magnitude standards may somewhat alter the ratio.

Bernheimer, *Lund Obs. Circ.*, No. 9 (1934). The newer surveys at the Lick and Palomar observatories reveal numerous clouds of galaxies with members fainter than magnitude 18.

8. A. E. Whitford, *Ast. Jour., 58*, 49 (1953); *59,* 194 (1954).

Region D. The south galactic polar zone. More than twenty workers throughout many years have had a share in the researches on galaxies of the south galactic polar zone. The results have been summarized in five short papers, in which some of the basic properties of the Inner Metagalaxy have been reported on. The distribution of the 80,000 galaxies from galactic latitude −60° to the south galactic pole, and conclusions based on the photometry of 31,000 of these objects, will be discussed in Chapter 5. Here we mention four points that appear to be of considerable significance.

1. The patrol cameras show an extremely smooth distribution of faint stars over the whole of this polar zone, indicating freedom from effective irregular space absorption.[9]

2. From the measures of magnitude and the relation

$$\log \bar{N}_m = b(m - m_1),$$

where $\bar{N}_m$ is the average number of galaxies per square degree to apparent magnitude m, the average space-density parameter m_1 is found to be 15.16 ± 0.02 (mean error), and the radial density gradient b is 0.592 ± 0.09 (m.e.). This value of b shows that metagalactic space out to the distance of 150 million light years is uniformly populated with galaxies, at least in this polar region encompassing nearly 3,000 square degrees. This conclusion holds for galaxies of average and brighter luminosity, but not necessarily for the little-known dwarfs.

3. No dependence of the frequency of galaxies on galactic latitude is found for latitudes between −55° and −90°.

4. A strong transverse density gradient appears to cross the polar zone, with the population increasing as we go southeastward toward the galactic circle. This gradient indicates a metagalactic cloud of galaxies more than a hundred million light years in extent; but with a deeper census it may tend to melt into the background.

Region E. The declination +43° belt. The south galactic polar zone passes directly overhead for the telescopes on Harvard Kopje, South Africa. This circumstance aids in the researches on southern galaxies. The corresponding advantage of zenithal work on northern galaxies has been attained through the study with the telescopes at the Agassiz Station (terrestrial latitude +42°.5) of the galaxies in a belt

9. *Pub. Ast. Soc. Pac., 65,* 237–41 (1953); see also Chapter 14 below.

of the sky between declinations $+41°$ and $+46°$. To test again the effect of latitude on galaxy distribution, a homogeneous set of plates was made at that station with the Metcalf doublet, completely covering this $5°$ belt. In the interest of uniformity, the plates have been examined and measured by one observer. Of the 22,300 galaxies marked on the 44 plates, the magnitudes were estimated for only the 17,700 in the central nine square degrees of each plate, where corrections for distance from the optical axis can be ignored.

The good determination of the latitude effect in the northern galactic hemisphere provided by this material, and the measure it gives of a radial density gradient, are discussed in Chapter 8.

Region F. The Canopy survey. The region of the northern sky extending broadly from the north galactic polar zone to the celestial north pole and beyond is unusually rich in bright galaxies. It includes most of the conspicuous objects in Ursa Major, Canes Venatici, Cameolopardalis, Boötes, and Coma Berenices. H. D. Curtis called this area the Canopy of Galaxies. Most of its conspicuous members lie between fifteen and twenty million light years distant. The part of the Canopy north of declination $+41°$ and with galactic latitude higher than $+20°$, a total of 3,600 square degrees, has been surveyed from the standpoint of surface distribution; magnitudes are available for only a part of the area. Its population of 78,000 galaxies provides data for the statistical examination of small-scale irregularities in distribution for this portion of the sky; and it provides also a good indication of the dust cloud obscuration along one border of the northern Milky Way. The Canopy overlaps a part of Region A, described above, and cuts across Region E in the higher northern galactic latitudes. (Chapter 7, § III.)

Region G. Galaxies through a Milky Way window. The method of measuring the dimensions of the galactic system through the joint use of galaxies and faint variable stars was inaugurated in the study of the southern variable star field VSF 233, centered in right ascension 17^h 36^m, declination $-59°$. In this low-latitude field of about 80 square degrees, 700 galaxies brighter than the 18th magnitude were found. The result was unexpected since the region is in low galactic latitude, $-12°$ to $-20°$, and the center of the field is but $30°$ from the center of our Galaxy.

Through this "window" Miss Swope has found and studied 200 variable stars, of which 28 per cent are of the RR Lyrae type. The median apparent magnitudes of these variables can be used to measure distances, after appropriate correction for whatever space absorption there may be. The number of galaxies detectable in a field is of course an indication of the degree of transparency. (Chapter 11.)

Other windows along the Milky Way merit careful examination for variable stars and galaxies. Few will be as free of absorption as VSF 233, if their latitudes are low. One noted recently in Centaurus will also be reported in Chapter 11, as well as one in Telescopium that contributes effectively to the measuring of the galactic radius. Another, in the second quadrant of galactic longitude (λ 90° to λ 180°), is under study, since the faint cepheid-family variables of the Taurus-Auriga-Perseus region are the best indicators we have of the extent of the Milky Way in the anti-center direction.

Region H. Seventy-nine hundred galaxies in Horologium. The first considerable study of the correlation of brightness with angular size among the distant galaxies was carried out in 1935 for the clusters and large agglomerations found in the survey of 174 square degrees in the southern constellations of Horologium, Dorado, and Reticulum. In these groupings of galaxies the differences in distance may be assumed to be relatively unimportant, and the angular sizes can be taken as proportional to linear dimensions.

The correlation coefficient between apparent magnitude and angular diameter, and its small standard deviation, for 1,322 galaxies in loose clusters, are

$$r = -0.272$$
$$\sigma = \ \ \ 0.026.$$

Although the coefficient is not large, the tendency of faint galaxies to be small is definite. Apparent brightness is, as naturally expected, at least a rough indicator of distance. The Horologium clusters are not like the rich and fairly symmetrical Coma group; rather, they are merely condensations in a great cloud of galaxies which has a total population of well over 10,000 individuals. In Chapter 9 such aggregates are further considered.

Region J. The catalogues of R. H. Baker. In the Fornax-Eridanus region of the southern sky (right ascension 2^h to 4^h, declination $-15°$

to —35°) Professor Baker has measured the positions, magnitudes, and dimensions of 2,098 galaxies. From the integrated apparent magnitude m and diameter d (in minutes of arc) he computed for each system a surface brightness m_s expressed in magnitudes and defined by [10]

$$m_s = -2.5 \log b_s$$
$$b_s = k b_t d^2 F$$
$$m_s = m_t - 10 + 5 \log d + 2.5 \log F$$

where b_t is total brightness and F, the form on a numerical scale from 1 to 10, is ten times the ratio of minor to major axis of the elliptical photographic image; k is an arbitrary constant. He found a range in the surface brightness, from magnitude 12 to 17, corresponding to a ratio of 100 to 1 in luminosity per unit area. The measures by Baker, as for my work in Region H, were based on long-exposure plates for which the scale is 1 mm = 1′.

Region K. The census in Coma and Virgo. The first methodical studies at Harvard of the magnitudes, classes, and positions of faint galaxies were carried through with the assistance of Adelaide Ames in an extension of our investigation of the bright galaxies over the whole sky. Working with four Bruce plates in the extremely rich northern galactic polar zone, Miss Ames measured 2,778 galaxies, including much of the bright Virgo cluster. The area, as shown in Figure 1, lies within Region C, described above; but in Region C the faint galaxies were only counted, not individually measured for position, brightness, and type.

In analyzing the Coma-Virgo results we found that the simple Lundmark and Hubble classification schemes for bright galaxies could not be used successfully for the fainter systems. Distinct differences, however, are easily discernible for these faint objects. They seemed to merit more individual attention than is given by lumping them together in the category of "unclassified." We therefore set up the Bruce system of classification. The *shape* of the photographic image and the degree of *central condensation* are the two definitive characteristics. (Occasional deviations are recognized as *irregularities* in texture or form.) We put the forms of the images into ten categories, based on the ratio of the minor axis to the major axis of the quasi-elliptical

10. See *Harv. Bul.,* No. 869 (1929).

photographic images. In practice, the most elongated form is 10 $b/a = 1$; the circular image is 10 $b/a = 10$. The concentration classes run from Class a (smooth, without central nucleus) to Class f (most concentrated).

The Bruce classification has not proved to be widely useful. No clear correlation of class with size, brightness, or cluster affiliation has yet appeared,[11] but the study has not been carried far. Bruce classifications have been published at Harvard only for regions H, J, and K; apart from this the system has been used only at Heidelberg.

In this early Coma-Virgo probe we had our first look at the relative frequencies of galaxy types and at the irregularities in the distribution of faint systems. At that time, in *Harvard Annals, 88,* No. 1 (1930), we foreshadowed some of the other characteristics of the Metagalaxy that have since been identified on the basis of the more extensive surveys described above.

Region L. Outlining the celestial smog of the southern Milky Way. The last of our large surveys undertaken at the Harvard Observatory covers one-fifth of the sky and shows the width of the Region of Obscuration along the Milky Way from longitude 200° to longitude 340°, and between latitudes −30° and +30°. A relatively narrow band of obscuration between 210° and 260° is revealed by the galaxy counts. The work and the deductions therefrom are reported fully in Chapter 10.

C. Summary

The metagalactic surveys with Harvard cameras at the southern and northern stations have completely covered the sky, but only in about one-fourth of the area have we examined individual galaxies in some detail. The eleven regions selected for the work on individual faint galaxies are distributed in such a way that we derive a reasonably good picture of the Metagalaxy. Of the million galaxies photographed with the Harvard telescopes, approximately 335,000 enter our study of the characteristics of distribution, of magnitude frequency, and, in some of the selected regions, of galaxy types. The most important

11. In the remote Coma cluster, however, the galaxies preferentially appear to be much flattened spheroids, about 2c or 3c on the Bruce classification, or perhaps E4 to S0 on the Hubble system. Cf. Spitzer and Baade, *Astroph. Jour., 113,* 413–18 (1951).

surveys are five: the two at and near the galactic poles; the survey in a northern belt five degrees wide extending around the sky; the census of a northern area of 3,600 square degrees (the Canopy) which involves several hundred of the brightest galaxies and 75,000 of the fainter; and the survey along the borders of the southern Milky Way.

Among the results derived from these surveys are the following:

1. The depth reached in the various investigations is estimated to be 150 million light years for galaxies of average luminosity and mass; it is greater for the giant systems like our own, and is much smaller for the extreme dwarfs.

2. Out to a distance of 10^8 light years the northern galactic hemisphere is considerably more populous than the southern—a phenomenon that has long been known for the brightest galaxies.

3. In the distribution of faint galaxies we find important density gradients which appear to be more basic in metagalactic structure than are the numerous clusters of galaxies that are revealed by the various surveys. But the future extension of the census beyond the 19th apparent magnitude with Schmidt telescopes may smooth out some of these large irregularities in population.

4. The galaxy surveys are, of course, seriously affected by the dark absorbing clouds along the Milky Way; the galaxies, however, are most useful in outlining the width and nature of the Zone of "Avoidance," which blots from our records nearly half of the galaxies that we properly assume to exist. (See, for example, Chapters 7, 8, and 10.)

All of the foregoing statements will be discussed and supported by observational data in later chapters.

CHAPTER 3. THE THOUSAND
BRIGHTEST GALAXIES

Ours is the brightest galaxy, of course, in appearance if not in fact, since it surrounds us on all sides and includes the sun and all naked-eye stars. From our viewpoint it outshines all the others. Also it is relatively very large and massive, but in spite of appearance it is not the highest in candle power. The Andromeda Nebula may be no smaller, and some of the giant galaxies in the distant groups described in Chapter 9 have higher absolute luminosities; they appear to be substantially brighter than absolute magnitude −18.5, the value suggested cautiously for our own spiral.

A. Deception

We tend to sort out galaxies of largest mass and highest population when we catalogue the thousand most conspicuous systems. Because of this sorting we are likely to deceive ourselves. The sample is misleading if we seek to know accurately the relative proportion of the various galaxy types, or to find the correct average dimensions, masses, and luminosities of galaxies throughout space. In surveys limited by apparent magnitude we almost completely ignore the numerous dwarfs. In consequence we may be misled, as a subsequent tabulation indicates, into believing that spirals comprise the most common type of galaxy.

In our catalogue of the thousand brightest galaxies,[1] which includes many as remote as twenty million light years, we find fewer than one-third of the members of what is called our local family—that is, we find less than one-third of the systems now known to be within two million light years. The excluded family members either are too faint to be picked up in a cataloguing of the thousand brightest, which are the thousand with apparent photographic magnitudes brighter than 12.8 (revised), or were omitted because of low surface brightness and consequent difficulty of discovery and measurement on our photographs. Of the six local galaxies that are included, three are spirals.

1. Harlow Shapley and Adelaide Ames, *Harv. Ann.*, *88*, No. 2 (1932).

But of the thirteen not included, none is a spiral. In our fairly well explored local neighborhood, therefore, spirals are actually in a decided minority, less than 20 per cent, although in the listing of the thousand brightest galaxies a large majority are spirals.

There is, of course, a similar deception associated with a census of stars brighter than a given magnitude; perhaps it is even worse. Scarcely any reddish dwarfs are found among the 5,000 naked-eye stars; but when the neighborhood of the sun is thoroughly explored telescopically—for example, all the space covered within sixteen light years [2]—we find that two-thirds of the population of about 50 is composed of dwarf M stars, none of them brighter than the 7th apparent magnitude. In the solor neighborhood giant stars are very scarce. The red Lilliputians are dominant. Our sun is thus far above average candle power among the 50 nearest in our neighborhood; but it is far below average when compared with the 50 most conspicuous naked-eye stars. A magnitude-limited census, whether of stars or galaxies, preferentially selects the giants and superigants. A true census of the population depends on complete space coverage rather than apparent magnitude.

If we are interested in a census (and an evolutionary study) of all stars or galaxies, we must remember this obstacle which is introduced by the spread of real luminosity and is specifically due to the relatively low luminosity of dwarf stars and dwarf galaxies and to their consequent inaccessibility.

But if it is in the distribution of the mass of cosmic material that our interest lies, and not simply in the number of stellar or galactic packages, we are in a better situation. The giant stars and the giant galaxies are attainable over vast reaches of space where dwarf stars and galaxies must remain unknown; but a giant star averages at least ten times the mass of a red dwarf, and our own giant galaxy has a hundred times the luminosity and mass of the dwarf galaxies of our neighborhood. In other words, the relatively small amount of mass contributed by dwarfs can be more safely neglected in considerations of total masses, and of galactic dynamics.

2. Peter van de Kamp, *Pub. Ast. Soc. Pac., 65,* 73–7 (1953).

B. *The most conspicuous*

The 30 brightest galaxies, not including our own, are presented in Table 2 in order of increasing right ascension. Seventeen of the 30 are familiar Messier objects. The majority are in the northern celestial hemisphere, and in northern galactic latitude—a reflection of the dominance locally of the Virgo and Ursa Major clouds of bright galaxies. The apparent magnitudes in the sixth column are based chiefly on photoelectric measures reduced to the photographic scale. The sources are Pettit's continuation [3] of the Stebbins-Whitford program,[4] the "focus and out-of-focus" measures on Mount Wilson photographs by Holmberg,[5] and, for the southernmost objects, adjusted estimates from Harvard patrol camera plates as recorded in the Shapley-Ames catalogue.

The most striking feature of the tabulation of the 30 brightest is the distribution of types (Hubble's classification): Sa, 1; Sb, 9; Sc, 9; all spirals, 19; E, 6 (of which 4 are called "peculiar"); and I, 5. Sixty per cent are spirals. Probably all of the spirals and several of the others, such as the irregular Messier 82 and the Large Magellanic Cloud, are massive well beyond the average and of high integrated luminosity. They get into this list even when at great distances. But the Sculptor and Fornax superclusters and the companions of the Andromeda Nebula, *NGC* 205 and *NGC* 221, are dwarfish galaxies that get into the list of 30 brightest only through being close at hand.

The peculiarity (p) affecting these four faint spheroidal objects is the looseness of internal structure—slight in *NGC* 205, extreme in the Sculptor supercluster. This loose spheroidal type appears very rarely among the thousand most conspicuous galaxies, but in a specific volume of space, as we shall later emphasize, it may be the most frequent form. Probably the words "peculiar" and "typical" should be interchanged when we make an all-cosmos census, for it seems likely that the dwarf spheroidal is a more representative type, and the

---

3. Edison Pettit, *Astroph. Jour.*, *120*, 413–38 (1954).

4. Joel Stebbins and Albert E. Whitford, *Astroph. Jour.*, *115*, 284–91 (1952). See also Whitford, *Astroph. Jour.*, *83*, 424 (1936).

5. Erik Holmberg, *Medd. Lund Obs.*, Ser. II, No. 128 (1950); and personal letters.

Table 2. The Thirty Brightest External Galaxies

Name	Position 1950.0 R.A.	Dec.	Galactic Latitude	Type	Magnitude H.C.O.	Holm.*	Messier Number
NGC 55	0^h 12^{m}5	−39° 30′	−77°	Scp	6.7:		
205	37.6	+41 25	−21	E5p	9.0	8.89	
221	40.0	+40 36	−22	E2p	9.2	9.06	32
224	40.0	+41 0	−20	Sb	4.3	4.33	31
253	45.1	−25 34	−88	Sc	6.0:		
Small Mag. Cloud	50	−73	−45	I	2.8:		
Sculptor cl.	55.4	−34 14	−83	E0p	8.8:		
NGC 598	1 31.1	+30 24	−31	Sc	6.3	6.19	33
Fornax cl.	2 35.6	−34 53	−64	E0p	9.1:		
NGC 1068	2 40.1	− 0 14	−51	Sb	10.0	9.63	77
Large Mag. Cloud	5 26	−69	−33	I-SB	1.2:		
NGC 2403	7 32.0	+65 43	+30	Sc	9.0	8.81	
3031	9 51.5	+69 18	+42	Sb	7.9	7.85	81
3034	51.9	+69 56	+42	I	9.3	9.20	82
3627	11 17.6	+13 17	+65	Sb	9.6	9.59	66
4258	12 16.5	+47 35	+69	Sb	9.4:	8.83	
4321	20.4	+16 6	+76	Sc	9.8	10.08	100
4449	25.8	+44 22	+74	I	9.7	9.87	
4472	27.3	+ 8 16	+70	E1	9.4		49
4486	28.3	+12 40	+75	E0	9.8:		87
4594	37.3	−11 21	+51	Sa	9.1	9.17	104
4631	39.8	+32 49	+84	Sc	9.8:	9.63	
4736	48.6	+41 23	+76	Sb	8.9	8.84	94
4826	54.3	+21 47	+82	Sb	9.3	9.19	64
4945	13 2.4	−49 1	+12	Sbp	8.0:		
5055	13.5	+42 17	+74	Sb	9.2	9.18	63
5194	27.8	+47 27	+68	Sc	8.9	8.88	51
5236	34.3	−29 37	+32	Sc	7.0:		83
5457	14 1.4	+54 35	+60	Sc	8.5	8.20	101
6822	19 42.1	−14 53	−20	I	9.2	9.21	

* The magnitudes of the penultimate column have been communicated by Erik Holmberg, who would add the following as brighter than the 10th magnitude: NGC 628, 9.74; NGC 2903, 9.48; NGC 6946, 9.67. The systematic difference, H.C.O. − Holm., is 0.06 mag.

giant compact spheroidal galaxy, commonly called typical, is infrequent and thus peculiar. Comparable in abundance with the dwarf spheroidals may be the dwarf irregular galaxies, like *NGC* 6822 and *IC* 1613, and those of the type of *IC* 3475 reported by Reaves as numerous in the Virgo Cloud.

Further investigation of the magnitudes of the fainter objects of Table 2 and of the marginal objects omitted from it may eventually alter the listing somewhat for galaxies fainter than the 9th magnitude.

C. The Shapley-Ames catalogue

The Harvard catalogue of bright galaxies was undertaken, in collaboration with Adelaide Ames, to provide a comprehensive survey of the positions, magnitudes, and types of galaxies for the brighter objects of the metagalactic system, for which previously no general photometry had been available. Some lists of northern systems, generally with rough visual magnitudes, had been compiled.[6] Reliable magnitude estimates for southern galaxies were completely lacking. We undertook to construct a uniform photometric survey of the whole sky. The equipment at the Boyden Station in Peru (later in South Africa), and at the Agassiz Station for the northern hemisphere, made it possible to cover the sky evenly, with essentially identical cameras in the south and north.

Such a catalogue, with positions, types, and magnitudes for the galaxies brighter than the 13th magnitude, should provide a suitable basis, we decided, for the study of the distribution of average galaxies out to a distance of several million light years. It should provide information also on the relative frequency of the types of galaxies, on the clustering of the nearest ones, and on the effect of the obscuring cosmic dust clouds in low galactic latitudes. But for the reasons given above it would contain only a few of the dwarf spheroidal and irregular galaxies.

6. The Dreyer catalogues (*NGC* and *IC*) do not give magnitudes, nor does the Reinmuth reworking of the Herschel *General Catalogue* (*Veroff. der Sternwarte zu Heidelberg, 9,* 1926). The principal photometric lists are J. Holetschek, *Ann. der Wiener Sternwarte, 20* (1907); Edwin Hubble, *Astroph. Jour., 64,* 321–69 (1926); Knut Lundmark, *Upsala Medd.,* No. 21 (1927); Björn Svenonius, *Ann. Lund Obs.,* No. 7, 152–60 (1938); Anders Reiz, *Ann. Lund Obs.,* No. 9, Appendix (1941); and the several Harvard catalogues mentioned in this chapter and Chapters 5–9.

After some experience in estimating the magnitudes of nebulous objects, we found that useful and dependable measures of the apparent brightness of galaxies could be obtained from the photographic plates of the Harvard sky patrol. The scale of the photographs is so small (1 mm = 10′) that the dimensions and texture of most nebular images are starlike enough for practical intercomparisons with stellar magnitude standards; the comparison is improved when the examining eyepiece is held slightly out of focus. The diameter of the patrol plate images of the 12th magnitude galaxies is usually around three or four minutes of arc, with nine-tenths of the light in a central core one minute in diameter.

The areas covered by the patrol plates are so large that each contains one or more magnitude sequences of the Kapteyn Selected Areas. Thus a set of fairly uniform reference standards on the international system is available. The customary exposure times of 60 to 90 minutes are suitable for the brightness interval between the 10th and 13th magnitudes in which 96 per cent of the thousand brightest galaxies lie. Eventually photoelectric magnitudes will be available for most of the galaxies brighter than 13. Pettit has made a survey [7] of many for which radial velocities have been measured by Humason at Mount Wilson and Palomar and by Mayall at the Lick Observatory. Earlier photoelectric work by Stebbins and colleagues [8] checked the Harvard photographic magnitude scale satisfactorily, but suggested a shift of the zero point of the Harvard magnitude system by −0.2. Current fundamental photometric research in this area is that of Holmberg and of Bigay. Out-of-focus work by the latter suggests that the inclusion of the outlying coronae of some of the brightest galaxies appreciably increases the apparent brightness,[9] but his photoelectric and photographic magnitudes between 10 and 13 show in the mean a correction to the Shapley-Ames values of only −0.1.

In a general revision and extension of the twenty-five-year-old catalogue, recently undertaken by Gerard de Vaucouleurs with the assistance of the Harvard Observatory, there will be a further consideration of the zero point, as well as many new magnitudes and types for individual galaxies. The revision will also include corrections of

7. See note 3.
8. See Stebbins and Whitford in note 4.
9. Joseph Bigay, *Ann. d'astroph.*, *14*, 319–82 (1951).

the relatively few errors in position. Some of the objects in the Shapley-Ames catalogue will be demoted because of faintness or error in identification, and possibly a few added. The catalogued magnitudes for those brighter than the 10th are not all dependable because of the unsuitability of the patrol plates for the larger objects. Holmberg's work, referred to above, and the photoelectric work at Mount Wilson by Pettit [10] and in France by Bigay and his colleagues [11] is preferable. For all kinds of photometry, however, the integrated magnitudes of objects brigher than the 10th are uncertain. The correction for the sky background, when the galaxies are large, is difficult, and the uncertain extent of the outlying nebulosity will continue to hamper the photometry, whether visual, photographic, extrafocal, with Schraffier-kasette, or photoelectric. Fortunately, however, for galaxies with magnitudes fainter than 10.5, fairly exact integrated measures are possible, and for them, especially when in groups like those in Fornax and Virgo, the accurate luminosities will be important in estimating masses, and in studying the dynamics of clusters and clouds of galaxies.

D. Angular dimensions of the larger galaxies

The surface brightness of galaxies differs conspicuously from one type to another and varies considerably within a type. As a consequence there is no close dependence of apparent brightness on size. A list of the brightest galaxies (as in Table 2) does not include all of the largest; and a list of the largest does not include all of the brightest. Only one-third of the 30 brightest galaxies (Table 2) are among the 31 with largest angular dimensions; the others, although bright, are compact. In Table 3, in order of right ascension, are the galaxies for which the diameters, measured on Harvard patrol plates and published in the Shapley-Ames catalogue, are equal to or greater than ten minutes of arc. Only seven of these have Messier numbers—NGC 224 (M 31), 598 (M 33), 3031 (M 81), 4258 (M 106), 5194 (M 51), 5236 (M 83), and 5457 (M 101).

A diameter in Table 3 refers only to the central part of a galaxy.

10. See note 3.
11. J. H. Bigay, R. Dumont, F. Lenouvel, M. Lunel, *Ann. d'astroph., 16,* 133–38 (1953), J. H. Bigay and R. Dumont, *Ann. d'astroph., 17,* 78–84 (1954).

Table 3. Galaxies with Angular Diameter of Ten Minutes of Arc and Larger (from Harvard Annals 88, No. 2 [1932])

Name		Position 1950.0		Magnitude *	Diameters	
		R.A.	Dec.			
NGC 45	0^h	11^m4	$-23°$ 27'	12.1:	10.0	7.0
55		12.5	-39 30	6.7:	25.0	3.0
224 †		40.0	$+41$ 0	4.3	160	40
247		44.6	-21 1	10.7	18.0	5.0
253		45.1	-25 34	6.0:	22.0	6.0
Small Mag. Cloud †		50	-73	2.8:	210	210
NGC 300		52.6	-37 58	11.3:	20	10
598 †	1	31.1	$+30$ 24	6.3	60	40
891	2	19.3	$+42$ 7	12.2:	12	1.0
Large Mag. Cloud †	5	26	-69	1.2:	430	430
NGC 2403	7	32.0	$+65$ 43	9.0	16	10
2683	8	49.6	$+33$ 38	10.8	10.0	1.0
2903	9	29.3	$+21$ 44	10.3	11.0	5.0
3031		51.5	$+69$ 18	7.9	16	10
3109	10	0.8	-25 55	11.2:	10.0	2.0
3628	11	17.7	$+13$ 53	11.3	12.0	1.5
4236	12	14.3	$+69$ 45	11.3:	23.0	6.0
4244		15.0	$+38$ 5	11.0	13.0	0.9
4258		16.5	$+47$ 35	9.4:	20.0	6.0
4395		23.4	$+33$ 49	11.4:	12	10
4517		29.0	$+$ 0 21	11.6:	10.0	1.0
4565		33.9	$+26$ 16	10.7	15.0	1.1
4631		39.8	$+32$ 49	9.8:	12.0	1.2
4656		41.6	$+32$ 26	11.3	20.0	. . .
4945	13	2.4	-49 1	8.0:	11.5	2.0
5128 †		22.4	-42 45	7.2:	10.0	8.0
5194		27.8	$+47$ 27	8.9	12.0	6.0
5236		34.3	-29 37	7.0	10.0	8.0
5457	14	1.4	$+54$ 35	8.5	22	22
5907	15	14.6	$+56$ 31	11.8	11.0	0.6
6822	19	42.1	-14 53	9.2	20	10

* The magnitudes in Table 2 are used for objects brighter than 10; otherwise from *Harv. Ann.*, 88, No. 2 (1932).

† The dim outlying parts are not included for these largest galaxies; similar extensions probably exist for most of the others of the table.

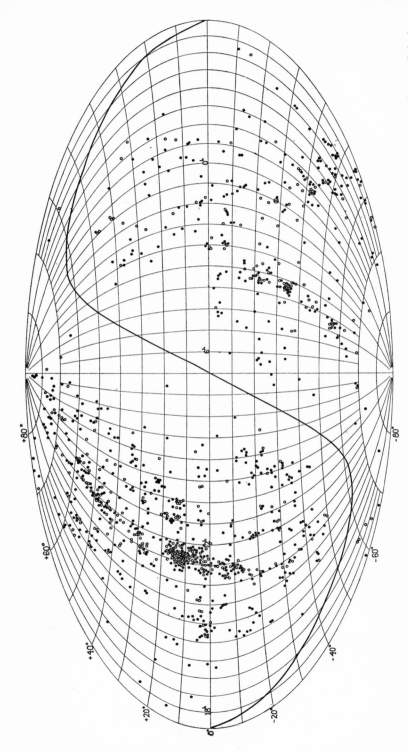

Figure 4. Distribution of bright galaxies on an Aitoff projection of the whole sky, with right ascension and declination as coordinates. Galaxies brighter than magnitude 12.0 are indicated by open circles. The heavy line is the projection of the galactic circle.

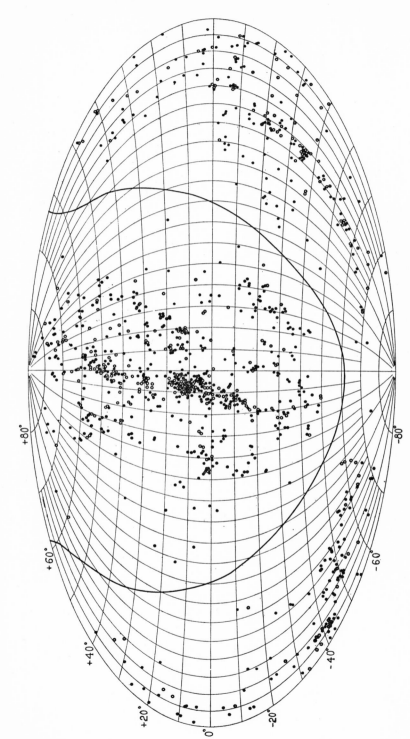

Figure 5. The same as Figure 4 with a shift of 6 hours in right ascension.

When these same objects are examined on long-exposure plates with larger cameras, as in our catalogue of Bruce telescope diameter measures,[12] the galaxies can be faintly traced to considerably greater distances from the centers. And if these photographic plates are measured with a microdensitometer, the deduced dimensions are still larger. The maximum and minimum diameters in Table 3 should be multiplied, on the average, by roughly 1.4 to reduce to the Bruce system, and by 2.2 to bring them up to the microdensitometer measures.

The ratio of microdensitometer diameters to the early Mount Wilson values is 4.1 on the average, but the increase in the measured diameters from the Mount Wilson estimates, or the Harvard estimates on patrol plates, to the microdensitometer readings depends on the class. Spheroidal systems show the greatest change. The important bearing of this revision of dimensions on the theory of the evolution of galaxies is discussed in Chapter 14.

E. The distribution of the brightest

The irregular and highly asymmetric distribution of the brightest galaxies, exhibited by the diagrams of the Shapley-Ames catalogue, was no surprise to the early workers on clusters and nebulae. The four diagrams are reproduced in Figures 4, 5, and 7. The photography and descriptions of the numerous spirals in Virgo, Ursa Major, and surrounding constellations—as carried on, for instance, at the Lick Observatory by Keeler and Curtis; in Heidelberg by Wolf and Reinmuth; at Mount Wilson by Pease, Hubble, Humason, and others; at Flagstaff by V. M. Slipher; in Lund by Lundmark and colleagues; at Helwan by Knox-Shaw and Madwar—all emphasized the uneven distribution of bright galaxies and called to attention the relative poverty of the south galactic hemisphere. The systematic Harvard survey on a magnitude basis was, however, the first to record clearly the actual state of affairs. Within its magnitude limits our catalogue was comprehensive. It excluded star clusters and diffuse nebulosities, but omitted few galaxies brighter than magnitude 12.9.

As their most striking feature the diagrams show that the northern galactic hemisphere is exactly twice as rich as the southern in galaxies brighter than the 13th magnitude. The unevenness holds at the 12th

12. *Harv. Ann., 88,* No. 4 (1934).

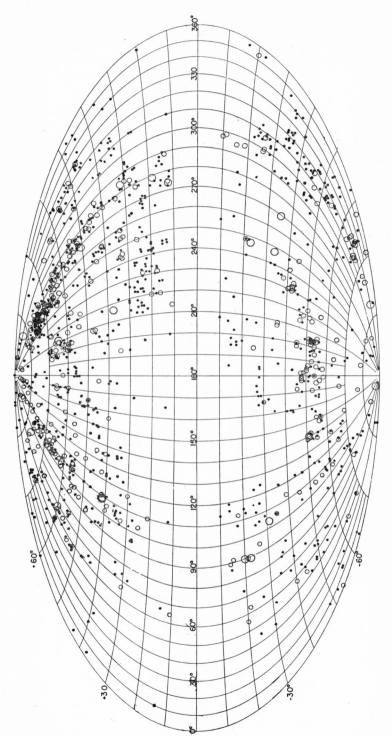

Figure 6. Distribution of bright galaxies with longitude and latitude as coordinates. Large circles for magnitudes brighter than 10.1; small circles, 10.1 to 12.0; dots, 12.1 to 13.0.

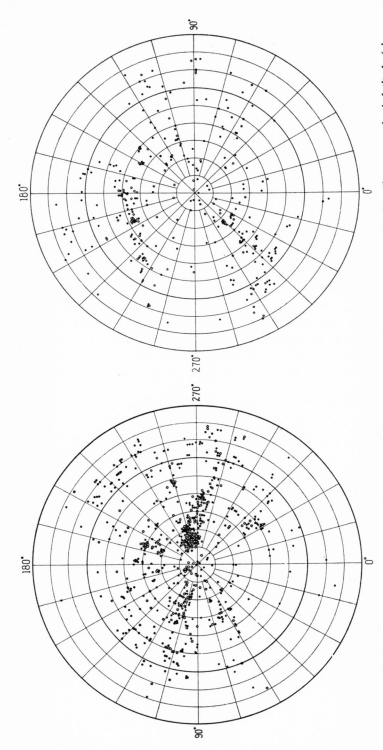

Figure 7. The distribution of the bright galaxies in the northern (left) and southern galactic hemispheres. Coordinates are galactic latitude (circular lines) and longitude (radial lines).

magnitude as well as the 13th, and the table shows that the doubling
holds roughly for all quadrants of galactic longitude.

Galactic	Brighter than Magnitude 12		Magnitude 12 to 13	
Longitude	North	South	North	South
0° to 90°	16	10	49	37
90 to 180	62	27	127	59
180 to 270	82	34	188	72
270 to 0	35	25	126	76
All	195	96	490	244

The plots in Figures 4 and 5 use equatorial coordinates. To show
better the relation of the distribution of these bright galaxies to the
Milky Way, Figure 6 exhibits the catalogue material in galactic coordinates. Figure 7 shows the two galactic hemispheres separately.

Conspicuous vacant regions appear in both hemispheres, in addition to the emptiness in low latitudes that results chiefly from the
obscuring matter in and around our Galaxy. (Within ten degrees of
the galactic circle there are no bright galaxies.) But a study of long-
exposure plates has shown that in most of the high-latitude vacant

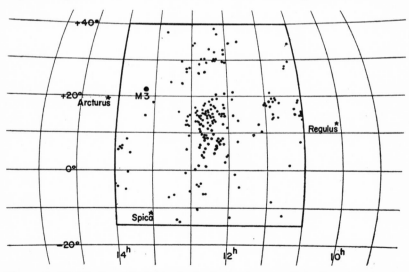

Figure 8. Distribution of bright galaxies in the Arcturus-Spica-Regulus triangle.
From Hardcastle's examination of the Franklin-Adams photographs of the
Coma-Virgo region

areas an approximately normal number of the fainter objects appears; and they are normal—not of unusual diameter or reddened. We therefore conclude that in latitudes greater than 30° the bright galaxy deficiencies, like the clusterings, are real.

A striking feature in the distribution of bright galaxies is the great Virgo Cloud near the north galactic pole, and the Fornax and other groupings in the southern galactic hemisphere. A discussion appears in Chapter 9 of the Virgo aggregation, to which much attention has been given in the past, and to which more will be given in the future in detailed analyses of the nearer parts of the Metagalaxy. Here we shall only point out that the Virgo Cloud is not simply the grouping of relatively bright galaxies centered at right ascension 12^h 30^m, declination $+12°$, but is a "supergalaxy" that extends southward at least 30°. In Figure 8 the distribution is shown first for the galaxies marked on the Franklin-Adams charts [13] and then in Figures 9 and 10 for galaxies to magnitude 12.3 and 12.9 respectively. The over-all length of this Virgo Cloud is at least ten million light years.

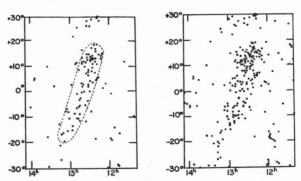

Figure 9 (*left*). The distribution of the galaxies brighter than magnitude 12.3 in and around the constellations Coma and Virgo. The dotted line indicates the approximate bounds of the extended Virgo cloud of galaxies.

Figure 10 (*right*). The distribution of galaxies brighter than magnitude 12.9 for the same region as in Figure 9

North of the densest portion of the Virgo Cloud, which is on the border of the constellation Coma, is that wide spreading of bright galaxies, the Canopy of H. D. Curtis. A rich central section of the Canopy, shown best in Figure 5, appears as a loose northern extension

13. J. A. Hardcastle, *Mon. Not. Roy. Ast. Soc., 74,* 699–707 (1914).

of the elongated "supergalaxy" in Virgo, and this arrangement, which imagination can easily couple with a string of bright galaxies in the southern hemisphere (Fig. 7), has led to the surmise that we have here an indication of a metagalactic circle and plane. The analogy with the galactic circle and plane for stars has strengthened the surmise that we have near us a flattened higher system of galaxies. Some support for the hypothesis has come from the work of Kraus and associates while recording radio signals in all galactic latitudes.[14]

An early worker in the field of galactic distribution was W. E. Bernheimer at the Lund Observatory, who pointed out the existence of a stream of galaxies and galaxy groups extending from Perseus into Pegasus. With K. Lundmark he found among the *NGC* objects several streams of galaxies and concluded that 25 per cent are in higher organizations.[15]

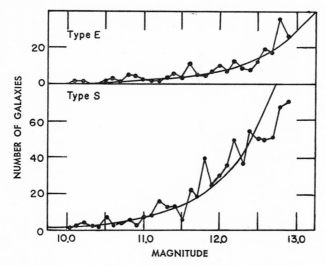

Figure 11. Frequency of galaxy types in tenth-of-a-magnitude intervals. Ordinates, number of objects; abscissae, photographic magnitudes

There seems to be little doubt of the existence of these associations, such as the Virgo plus Virgo Extension and the Bernheimer

14. John D. Kraus, *Ast. Jour.*, 59, 113–16 (1954).

15. Walter E. Bernheimer, *Nature, 130*, 132 (1932), *Die Himmelswelt, 42*, 223 (1932), Fig. 2, and *Forschungen und Forschriften, 9*, No. 16, 236–37 (1933).

supersystem; but taking the survey to fainter magnitudes erases much of the evidence of a basic metagalactic plane. These clusters and clouds of galaxies appear to be assemblages of only local significance. Too much has been read into the distribution of a few hundred galaxies while ignoring the distribution of the thousands just fainter. In much the same fashion spiral structure and "lines of cleavage" were read into globular clusters some sixty years ago on the basis of the distribution of the few hundred brightest stars.[16]

F. General luminosity curves for the thousand brightest

The number of galaxies of the two principal types for each tenth of a magnitude interval is shown in Table 4, and graphically in Figures

Table 4. The Frequency of Magnitudes

Photographic Magnitude	Type E	Type S	Photographic Magnitude	Type E	Type S
]10.0	2	14	11.5	3	6
10.0	. .	1	.6	11	22
.1	1	2	.7	5	19
.2	1	3	.8	5	40
.3	. .	2	.9	7	25
.4	. .	2	12.0	10	30
10.5	1	7	.1	7	35
.6	2	3	.2	12	49
.7	1	4	.3	9	28
.8	5	5	.4	8	54
.9	4	3	12.5	12	51
11.0	2	7	.6	20	50
.1	1	8	.7	17	51
.2	1	16	.8	36	67
.3	3	13	.9	26	71
.4	5	13	]13.0	217	701

11 and 12. Notwithstanding the great irregularities in surface distribution in many sections of the sky, a close approach to constant frequency per unit volume of space is attained when large sections of the sky or the whole of it are considered. The smooth curves drawn separately in Figures 11 and 12 for spheroidal and spiral galaxies indicate the population that would prevail if there were uniform distribution in depth: the number of galaxies should double for each half magnitude.

16. *Mt. Wilson Contr.*, No. 115, 5 (1915).

The deviations from the smooth curves amount to 50 per cent at some magnitudes, no doubt recording irregularities in depth similar to those on the surface. Fainter than magnitude 12.5, the galaxies recognized as spiral fall short of the theoretical curve, whereas the spheroidal galaxies more than maintain the population trend. Possibly this circumstance indicates only our failure to recognize the spirality of some of the objects now classed as either spheroidal or of unrecognized type. The essential completeness of the catalogue to magnitude 12.9 is verified by the plot of the frequencies of magnitudes when all types are brought together (Fig. 12).

Before we look into the problem of metagalactic population and structure as depicted by the innumerable galaxies fainter than the 13th magnitude, we shall examine in some detail the characteristics of the two nearest external galaxies, the Magellanic Clouds, which fortunately are near enough for detailed exploration by observers in the southern hemisphere.

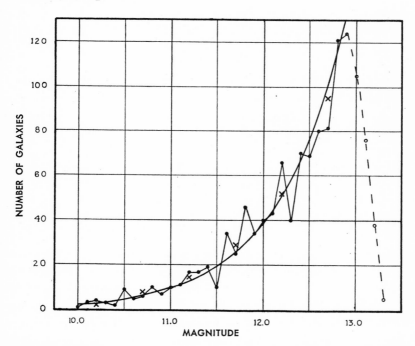

Figure 12. Frequency curve for all types of bright galaxies in tenth-of-a-magnitude intervals. Crosses indicate mean values. Smoothed curves in Figures 11 and 12 represent hypothetical uniform density in space.

CHAPTER 4. THE STAR CLOUDS OF MAGELLAN—A GATEWAY TO THE METAGALAXY [1]

Those who have undertaken to explore and interpret the Metagalaxy have been favored with several special leads and advantages. Among these advantages are the great age of the crust of the earth, the human sense of history (that is, our ability to record and recall events in a time sequence), the relative proximity of the Virgo Cloud of galaxies, the high transparency of the earth's gaseous envelope in the visual and short-wave radio sections of the electromagnetic spectrum, and —of immediate value to cosmic exploration—the availability of the nearby Star Clouds of Magellan. This spread of favorable circumstances is wide and varied, but here our only concern is with the pair of star aggregates called the Magellanic Clouds. We shall try to show why they have much significance for inquiries about the universe.

A. Introductory on our Galaxy and others

As recently as forty years ago A. S. Eddington pictured the stellar universe with a diagram that put the sun and its planetary family in the center (Fig. 13). The "flatness" of the system had long been recognized. The encircling Milky Way, which early in the 17th century was revealed to Galileo as star-composed, was the first clue to the discoidal shape. The faint stars were observed to be hundreds of times more numerous along the Milky Way girdle than at the poles, 90° from the Milky Way circle. Such a distribution could most reasonably mean a flattened system, and as long ago as the time of Thomas Wright and Immanuel Kant, in the middle of the 18th century, the Milky Way light was interpreted as wholly due to stars. Somewhat later Sir William Herschel's surveys substantiated the evidence beyond all doubting and confirmed the existence of millions of faint stars.

1. Under the title of "The Clouds of Magellan—A Gateway to the Sidereal Universe" this chapter was published in the *American Scientist* for January 1956 and is here reprinted by permission of the editors of the quarterly of the National Society of the Sigma Xi.

But the earth was rather naturally placed by these pioneers and subsequent investigators in a central location, as seemed to befit the self-proclaimed dignity and importance of man.

The Eddington picture did not long stand; and a decade later he expresed amazement that he could so recently have had such a primitive idea. The estimated distances of the eclipsing binaries, then under analysis at the Princeton Observatory, gave some surprisingly large values. Incredible distances were found for some of these members of a sidereal universe which up to then had been estimated by Newcomb and others to have a radius of only a few thousand light years. Then the giant cepheid variables yielded evidence that began to extend the boundaries still farther; and when the cepheids were found abundantly in globular star clusters, very faint because of distance, it became apparent that the accepted scale of the universe needed drastic revision.

Skipping the details for the moment, we note that by 1930 astronomers had found a number of astonishing facts about the universe; for example, the earth, sun, and naked-eye stars are thousands of light years from the center of our Milky Way; the spiral nebulae are great galaxies of stars (as Kant reasoned in 1750), and our own stellar system is a giant rotating spiral of stars, infused with much interstellar dust and gas. By 1930 we also knew that the myriads of galaxies are in a system that is expanding at great speed into a half-understood space. Instead of the few hundred light years of measurable distance available for the early Eddington concept of the sidereal universe, we had reached, fifteen years later, to distances of several hundred million light years. From busying ourselves about the stars in one sun-centered

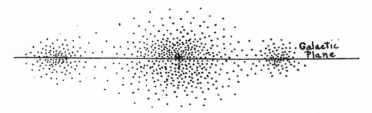

Figure 13. Eddington's early concept of the sidereal universe. The cross indicates the position of the sun. From A. S. Eddington, *Stellar Movements and the Structure of the Universe* (London, Macmillan, 1914), p. 31

"universe," we had become sensitive to the stellar problem of a million "island universes" and had begun to talk seriously about the origin of the stellar world and its destiny.

A great change had occurred rapidly, and three of the prime movers in that revolution in knowledge and cosmic concept were the large American telescopes, the relativity theory and its consequences, and the Star Clouds of Magellan. It is the aim of this chapter, as mentioned above, to report on the nature of these Clouds, tell what they have done for us, and explain how they helped to initiate the revision of our cosmic viewpoint. At the same time these pages will summarize many of the investigations of the Magellanic Clouds that have been carried on at the Harvard College Observatory during the past three decades.

In more than one sense the Magellanic Clouds serve as a gateway to the Metagalaxy—to the outer and over-all aggregate of galaxies. They are a pair of stellar systems of galaxy size. The analysis of their structures and contents leads us through technological gateways to knowledge of other galaxies that because of greater distance are less readily examined. Moreover, they are rich in all the sidereal entities— stars, gaseous nebulosity, star clusters, interstellar dust—which large systems like ours contain. They are indeed the most accessible entry to the Metagalaxy, and in themselves are subjects deserving close study for their illumination of the processes of stellar evolution. Celestial dynamics on a gross scale and cosmic chemistry are also indebted to these nearest of external galaxies.

B. Historical notes

The Star Clouds of Magellan were, of course, known thousands of years ago to the primitive star watchers in southern latitudes. But they got into the literature of travel and astronomy only as a by-product of the post-Columbian explorations of the southern terrestrial hemisphere. A few quotations will present the observations and interpretations which they incited in earlier centuries.

Thus Peter Martyr:

But it is most certeyne, that it is not gyuen to anye one man to knowe all thynges. . . .

Neuerthelesse, the Portugales of owre tyme haue sayled to the fyue and fyftie degree of the south pole: Where, coompasinge abowte the poynt thereof, they myght see throughowte al the heauen about the same, certeyne shynynge whyte cloudes here and there among the starres, lyke vnto theym whiche are seene in the tracte of heauen cauled *Lactea via,* that is, the mylke whyte waye. They say, there is noo notable starre neare about that pole lyke vnto this of owres which the common people thynke to bee the pole it selfe. . . . When therefore it is autumne with vs, it is sprynge tyme with them: And summer with vs when it is wynter with them. But it suffiseth to haue sayde thus much of strange matters.[2]

Antonio Pigafetta:

They consydered in this nauigation that the pole Antartike hath no notable starre after the sorte of the pole Artike. But they sawe many starres gathered togyther, whyche are like two clowdes one separate a little from an other, and sum what darke in the myddest [Fig. 14].

Figure 14.
Pigafetta's diagram
of the south polar sky,
showing the
Magellanic Clouds

Betweene these, are two starres not very bigge, nor muche shynninge, whiche moue a little: And these two are the pole Antartike. . . . When they were in the myddest of the goulfe, they sawe a crosse of fiue clear starres directly toward the Weste, and of equall distance the one from the other.[3]

Vespucci and de Corsali:

Here we sawe a marueylous order of starres, so that in the parte of heauen contrary to owre northe pole, to knowe in what place and degree the south pole was, we tooke the day with the soonne, and obserued

2. Peter Martyr, *Decades,* trans. by Richard Eden in *The First Three English Books on America* (1511?–55), E. Arber, ed. (Birmingham, 1885), p. 142.
3. Antonio Pigafetta, *The Vyage abowte the Worlde,* in *ibid.,* p. 253.

the nyght with the Astrolabie, and sawe manifestly twoo clowdes of reasonable bygnesse mouynge abowt the place of the pole continually nowe rysynge and nowe faulynge, so keepynge theyr continuall course in circular mouynge, with a starre euer in the myddest which is turned abowt with them abowte xi degrees from the pole.[4]

Alexander von Humboldt:

The knowledge of the two Magellanic clouds has been unjustly ascribed to Pigafetta, for I find that Anghiera, on the observations of Portuguese seamen, mentions these clouds fully eight years before the termination of Magellan's voyage of circumnavigation. He compares their mild effulgence to that of the Milky Way. The larger cloud did not, however, escape the vigilance of the Arabs, and it is probably the white ox (*El Bakar*) of their southern sky . . .[5]

James Dunlop:

The Nebula Minor, to the naked eye, has very much the appearance of a small cirrus-cloud; and through the telescope, it has very much the appearance of one of the brighter portions of the milky way, although it is not so rich in stars of all the variety of small magnitudes, with which the brighter parts of the milky way in general abound, and therefore it is probably a beautiful specimen of the nebulosity of which the remote portion of that magnificent zone is composed. Plate IV [see Figs. 16 and 17] is a very correct drawing of the nebula, which if faithfully represented by the engraver, will convey a better idea of it than I could possibly hope to do by words.[6]

And Sir John Herschel:

The two Magellanic clouds, Nubecula major and Nubecula minor, are very remarkable objects. The larger of the two is an accumulated mass of stars, and consists of clusters of stars of irregular form, either conical masses or nebulae of different magnitudes and degrees of condensation. This is interspersed with nebulous spots, not resolvable into stars, but which are probably *star dust,* appearing only as a general radiance upon the telescopic field of a twenty-feet reflector, and forming

4. Amerigo Vespucci and Andes de Corsali, *Of the Pole Antarctic,* in *ibid.,* p. 279.

5. Alexander von Humboldt, *Cosmos,* trans. by E. C. Otté (2d ed. New York, 1847–48), *2,* 287.

6. James Dunlop, *"A Catalogue of Nebulae and Clusters of Stars in the Southern Hemisphere Observed at Paramatta in New South Wales,"* Phil. Trans. Roy. Soc. of London, *118,* 113–51 (1828).

a luminous ground on which other objects of striking and indescribable form are scattered. In no other portion of the heavens are so many nebulous and stellar masses thronged together in an equally small space. Nubecula minor is much less beautiful, has more unresolvable nebulous light, while the stellar masses are fewer and fainter in intensity.[7]

The account by Pigafetta served to attach the name of his master, the "great circumnavigator" Ferdinand Magellan, to the Nubeculae, and with few exceptions modern writers have accepted the designations.

The history of modern researches on the Clouds has been sketched by various writers [8] and told most completely in the memoir by Buscombe, Gascoigne, and de Vaucouleurs in the *Australian Journal of Science* for December 1954. The five decades of work on the Clouds by Harvard observers is there summarized briefly but so well that the present account need provide no detailed bibliography, nor an accounting of research methods. We are free to consider chiefly the general characteristics of the Clouds and devote some attention to the cosmic position of these galaxies that serve as the Magellanic Gateway.

Until recently nearly all the work on the Clouds of Magellan was done at the Boyden Station of the Harvard Observatory, first at Arequipa, Peru, and since 1927 in South Africa. Sir John Herschel and James Dunlop, more than a century ago, catalogued many of the clusters and nebulae, with brief descriptions, but after them nothing of consequence was accomplished in the study of the Clouds until the Harvard cameras near the end of the last century began to accumulate photographs.

A precocious early evaluation of the Magellanic Clouds and other "nebulae" was made in 1867 by Cleveland Abbe, distinguished American meteorologist, the "father of the Weather Bureau," who carried out a modest but penetrating study of Sir John Herschel's newly published *General Catalogue of Nebulae and Clusters of Stars* (1864). In four sentences he cautiously summarized his interpretation:

7. From a letter from Feldhuysen, Cape of Good Hope, June 13, 1836, printed in von Humboldt, *Cosmos, 1,* 85.

8. D. Wattenberg, *Ast. Nach., 237,* 401–12 (1929); Harlow Shapley, *Galaxies,* Blakiston, 1943; *Pub. Obs. Mich., 10,* 79–84 (1951) (Harv. Reprint, Ser. II, 37).

The study of the foregoing Tables may lead to the following conclusions or suggestions:

1. The Clusters are members of the *Via Lactea,* and are nearer to us than the average of its faint stars.

2. The Nebulae [galaxies] resolved and unresolved lie in general without the *Via Lactea,* which is therefore essentially stellar.

3. The visible universe is composed of systems, of which the *Via Lactea,* the two Nubeculae, and the Nebulae, are the individuals, and which are themselves composed of stars (either simple, multiple, or in clusters) and of gaseous bodies of both regular and irregular outlines.[9]

Fifty years later we caught up with Abbe and accepted the galaxy character of the Magellanic Clouds and the spirals; it was nearly another forty years before the Australian writers drew attention to this overlooked surmise of 1867.

The earlier Harvard work concerned the variable stars and the spectral classes of bright stars and nebulae—work that is chiefly associated with the names of Henrietta S. Leavitt and Annie J. Cannon. Subsequently many Harvard observers have worked extensively on the variables and to some extent on the nebulae, clusters, spectra, and motions.

Beginning in 1914 the Lick Observatory at its station in Chile measured the radial velocities of 17 bright-line nebulae in the Large Cloud and one in the Small. In recent years photoelectric photometry, color photography, small-scale spectroscopy, and radio telescopes have been turned to the problems of the Clouds. With the building of several new telescopes, their powerful spectrographs, and the giant antennae for radio exploration, a new epoch is opening for astronomical observations in the southern hemisphere. As a consequence these nearest of external systems should soon yield important new results on the evolution of stars and the development of galaxies.

C. General description

To the naked eye the Star Clouds of Magellan are not particularly impressive. They are patchy and indefinite in structure and light. Their individual stars are not discernible to the unaided eye or through small telescopes. But the merged radiation of their innumerable members accumulates to a total surface brightness much like that of the rich

9. Cleveland Abbe, *Mon. Not. Roy. Ast. Soc.,* 27, 262 (1867).

star clouds along the Milky Way. They form a triangle with the south celestial pole but serve to indicate true south less well than Polaris indicates true north. With a large field camera of short focus both Clouds may be recorded on a single photograph (Fig. 19a).

To show graphically, and in a sense dramatically, what lies beyond the Clouds, we plot in Figure 15 the distribution, as found on a Bruce camera photograph, of hundreds of the more distant galaxies, each of which is composed of its billions of stars. These galaxies here register dimly, on the long-exposure photographs, as tiny irregular patches of light, mostly too faint for the eye to see with any telescope. The upper right corner of this field borders the Large Cloud, of which the dark nebulosity appears to cut down by one-half the observable population of remote galaxies. The plot covers only a forty-fifth of one per

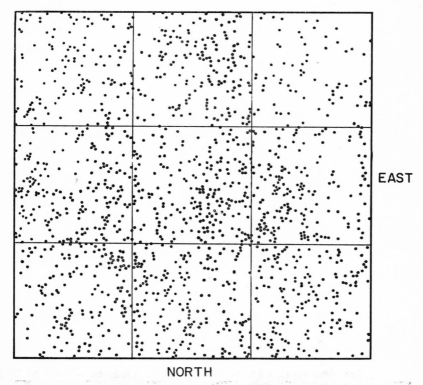

EAST

NORTH

Figure 15. The distribution of 1,450 galaxies over nine square degrees near the Large Magellanic Cloud

cent of the sky, but it records the 1,450 galaxies in this direction that are brighter than magnitude 17.7 and mostly more distant than a hundred million light years; it suggests how much lies beyond the Magellanic Gateway out in boundless metagalactic space.

The positions of the centers of the Clouds in equatorial and galactic coordinates are given in the table. The Large Cloud is mostly in Doradus and Mensa, the Small Cloud in Tucana. Their dimensions cannot be definitively stated. The "main body" of the Large Cloud (Fig. 19a) has a mean angular diameter of 7°, and the Small Cloud 4°. But these diameters increase to 12° and 8° when the outlying clusters and cepheids are recognized, and they are still larger when measured in terms of the permeating and surrounding clouds of neutral hydrogen gas, as reported by Frank Kerr and his colleagues at Sydney, Australia (Fig. 19b).

	Large Cloud	Small Cloud
Right ascension	$5^h 26^m$	$0^h 50^m$
Declination	—69°	—73°
Galactic longitude	247°	269°
Galactic latitude	—33°	—45°

The angular separation of the centers is approximately 21°, but the edges are probably less than 3° apart. The corresponding linear separations, in projection, are 60 k.l.y.[10] and 9 k.l.y., if we accept 170 k.l.y. as the distance. The cepheids show that the distances from the sun are nearly the same and therefore the foregoing values may be taken as the approximate actual linear separations. The over-all linear diameters of the two Clouds are 60 k.l.y. and 40 k.l.y., which should be compared with something more than 100 k.l.y. for our Galaxy.

It is also difficult to determine the total luminosity of a Magellanic Cloud because of its wide extent. It cannot be compared accurately with the neighboring bright stars even when out-of-focus methods are used. Also the estimated apparent brightness of any extended star cloud must be uncertainly corrected for superposed galactic stars. Some fair estimates of the total brightness have been made by way of integrations from photometer tracings across a cloud, or across photo-

10. The abbreviation k.l.y. used in this paper stands for a thousand light years, and m.l.y. (mega-light years) for a million.

graphs of a cloud. Values depending on photoelectric techniques will eventually provide an additional basis for estimating cloud luminosity. Perhaps it is not important to know the total radiation from these irregular Clouds of Magellan. There are many distant similar systems that will yield better indications of total light and mass because their photographic images are compact and enable us to place irregular galaxies with some confidence in the series of galaxy types. We shall here accept as provisional values:

Large Cloud 1.2 pg; Small Cloud 2.8 pg.

Visually they are somewhat brighter. Magnitudes 0.5 and 2.0 may be better values when all outlying stars are included. For comparison we note the following photographic magnitudes for some stars that are relatively bright because of nearness:

Achernar 0.4; Betelgeuse 2.5; Canopus −0.5; Sirius −1.6.

The bar or axis of the Large Cloud, which is its most distinctive feature, has naturally led to the Cloud's classification as a quasi-barred spiral. In time it may evolve toward regularity in its spiral arms. The Small Cloud, however, has much less claim to the barred-spiral category, and its evolutionary destiny may be a dwarfish spheroidal galaxy, like the Sculptor and Fornax "superclusters," rather than a spiral.

The 4th magnitude nebulosity 30 Doradus, of which we shall have more to say later, is visible to the unaided eye as a hazy feature of the Large Cloud.

D. The principal contributions

Other choices might well be made, but the writer would select the following as the four most important astronomical contributions associated with the Clouds of Magellan:

1. Discovery of hundreds of giant cepheid variables in both Clouds (Harvard, 1904+).

2. Measurement of high positive radial velocities for emission-line objects associated with the Clouds, suggesting their independence of the Milky Way (Lick). For a summarized report on R. E. Wilson's and W. J. Luyten's work on radial velocities and proper motions, respectively, see discussion in the treatise cited in note 26 below.

3. Discovery and development of the period-luminosity relation for classical cepheids (Harvard).

4. Detection with radio telescopes of neutral hydrogen in and around the Clouds, and the measurement of its distribution (Sydney).

Less important but still significant contributions include the following:

5. The finding of the maximum luminosities reached by stars of many spectral types; for example, by the novae and the variables of all principal classes, by open and globular clusters, and by planetaries and other bright-line nebulae (Harvard).

6. The demonstration of a peculiar frequency distribution of the periods of classical cepheids in the Small Cloud, with evidence of a marked dependence of period on stellar density (Harvard).

7. The derivation of a color-magnitude array for supergiant stars, brighter than $M_{pg} = -4$, in the Small Cloud (Columbia University).

8. Discovery of numerous bluish supergiant eclipsing stars of the Beta Lyrae type, many of which are associated with the great 30 Doradus nebula (Harvard).

9. Presentation of preliminary evidences of rotation and of internal turbulence in the Large Cloud (Lick and Sydney).

10. The deduction that the Clouds of Magellan are not dwarf associates of the Milky Way but are full-size galaxies, brighter and more massive than the average galaxy in our part of the universe (Harvard, Mount Wilson, et al.).

11. Conclusion that at least two types of stellar population occur in both Clouds: the primitive stars, with their presence indicated by the associated globular clusters, and the recently evolved stars, represented by the blue supergiants and suggested by the abundant bright and dark nebulosity (Pretoria, Harvard, et al.).

12. The deduction that the 30 Doradus bright nebulosity in the Large Cloud is more radiant by a hundred times than the brightest globular cluster known anywhere, and in fact is more luminous intrinsically than many of the nearby dwarf galaxies with their millions of stars (Harvard).

13. Discovery of a large "wing" of the Small Cloud (1940), and recently acquired (1955) evidence from the occurrence therein of only long-period supergiant cepheids that the wing may be, in a sense, a structure distinct from the Small Cloud; but the distances of

the two must now be essentially the same since the wing's variables fit the Small Cloud's period-magnitude relation (Harvard).

Altogether these thirteen items emphasize the usefulness of the "shynynge whyte cloudes" for our understanding of the sidereal universe. It is more than likely that additional contributions, now unforeseen, will come from further study of the Clouds with large instruments, and they may equal in importance those listed above.

E. Preliminary on the variable stars

The first of the hundreds of cepheid variable stars that have been found in the Magellanic Clouds were those discovered and marked on Boyden Station plates by Miss Leavitt in 1904. Seven years earlier Mrs. Fleming had detected the variability of the strange supergiant star S Doradus. By 1908 Miss Leavitt had listed 969 variable stars in the Small Magellanic Cloud and 808 in the Large Cloud.[11]

The numbers have now been increased to more than 2,000 in the Large Cloud and more than 1,500 in the Small; but for many such stars the variation is slight or uncertain and we prefer to say that the total variable star population now known, brighter than the 18th apparent magnitude, is approximately 3,000 in the two Clouds. With photographs of large scale, however, the number can be sensibly increased.

The periods of 25 selected variables in the Small Cloud were found by Miss Leavitt to be short in comparison with the periods of the variables that were better known at that time, namely the long-period variables headed by Mira (Omicron Ceti). She did not identify the Cloud variables with Delta Cephei and other known cepheids. The famous note in *Harvard Circular,* No. 173 (1912), which gives the early version of the period-magnitude relation, called the 25 stars simply short-period variables. Included with the description, however, was the shrewd statement, "Since the variables are probably at nearly the same distance from the Earth, their periods are apparently associated with their actual emission of light, as determined by their mass, density, and surface brightness. . . . A number of brighter variables have similar light curves, as UY Cygni, and should repay careful study.

11. Henrietta S. Leavitt, "1777 Variables in the Magellanic Clouds," *Harv. Ann., 60,* 87–108 (1908).

The class of spectrum ought to be determined for as many objects as possible. It is to be hoped, also, that the parallaxes of some variables of this type may be measured."

The identification of the variables as cepheids was soon made by E. Hertzsprung, then at Potsdam.[12] He noted the relatively very small proper motions of such stars in our own galactic system, and deducing therefrom their probably great distances and luminosities, he proceeded to derive a value of the parallax of the Small Cloud. A computational error in his report, which resulted in his stating that the Small Cloud is but 3,000 light years distant, may have contributed to the fact that the high significance of his deduction was not fully appreciated. The outside-of-the-galaxy character of the Clouds was definitely established when the period-luminosity curve had been developed, the center of the Milky Way located far off in the direction of Sagittarius, and the writer's estimate of a distance for the Clouds as more than 60,000 light years was announced. That the Clouds are separate from our Galaxy was also suggested by the large radial velocities found by the Lick observers.

Independently of their role in measuring distances, the cepheids of the Clouds have much to contribute. Chiefly the Bruce telescope at the Boyden Station, but also some of the other cameras, early provided material for the preliminary study of periods and light curves. The available objective prism plates showed spectra of the brightest cepheids and of other superluminous variable stars. For four decades the laborious study of the variables has proceeded at the Harvard Observatory. A report on the more important results gathered over the years by many workers is given in a later section of this chapter.

Virginia McKibben Nail has devoted more time to the variable stars and other Magellanic Cloud problems than any other observer. Since 1923 the late J. S. Paraskevopoulos and his associates at the Boyden Station have made a majority of the plates. Many of the earlier photographs were made by Solon I. Bailey and Leon Campbell. The principal discoverers of the variable stars, after Miss Leavitt, have been Mrs. Sylvia F. M. Lindsay and Mrs. Nail. Using 60-inch reflector plates, Martha Dowse found many of the fainter variables, particularly

12. E. Hertzsprung, *"Über die räumliche Verteil der Veränderlichen vom δ Cephei-Typus,"* Ast. Nach., *196,* 204 (1914).

in the Small Cloud. Other workers on the photographic plates include Adelaide Ames, Richard Craig, Dorrit Hoffleit, Jenka Mohr, Harvia Wilson, and Frances W. Wright.

F. Nebulae and supergiants

In addition to the variable stars several kinds of high-luminosity radiators appear in the Clouds. Hundreds of Magellanic stars are brighter than $M = -4.5$ (10,000 times the sun's luminosity). It is to be expected that such exceedingly luminous objects might show variability, since they lie in a part of the color-magnitude array where rapid evolution is probable. But even when their light as a whole is not measurably variable, such stars are undoubtedly beset with much turbulence and their spectra should reveal the differences between them and ordinary giant stars, or stars of the main sequence. This is in fact the situation. Many of the brightest supergiants have emission lines in their spectra as well as the typical absorption lines. Among them are the peculiar OB stars and some of the P-Cygni type. Superluminous long-period and irregular variables frequently exhibit emission lines, as also do the super-supergiant cepheids with periods greater than 30 days. The small-scale objective prism plates at Harvard permitted Miss Cannon to list such bright-line objects in her catalogues of spectra, and elsewhere. There would be little point in re-collecting the data at this time and in this place since in a few years spectra of higher dispersion will be available and the lists of peculiar stars can rapidly grow.

The various types of supergiants are exceptionally important in astrophysics. They show, for example, how large and luminous stars can be. Some individuals of the Clouds are more luminous than the total of a globular cluster that contains more than 100,000 stars. Until radial velocities are available for objects of magnitudes 10 to 13, we cannot accurately sort out from the foreground of ordinary galactic stars those supergiants in the Clouds that mark the maximum attainable for the various stellar types (except when spectral peculiarities reveal them). High radial velocities, of the order of $+170$ and $+275$ km/sec will, however, guarantee membership in the Small and the Large Cloud, respectively.

On provisional statistical grounds we can estimate that several hundred stars of the Large Cloud are brighter than apparent magnitude 12,[13] corresponding to absolute magnitudes brighter than —7 and to luminosities greater than 100,000 times that of the sun. Some of these are blue, more of them are reddish and frequently variable. The Small Cloud also has its supergiants, but they are not as numerous. In an early survey we found [14] that 20 or 30 stars of the Large Cloud are much brighter than magnitude 9.0 (therefore a million times the solar luminosity), but we noted that "any one of these excessively bright objects may, of course, actually be a compact group of many stars of similar spectral class." Even so the component stars must be supergiants. When they are reddish, their diameters exceed that of Jupiter's orbit.

A conspicuous feature of both Clouds is the display of nebular objects, with spectra dominated by bright lines of hydrogen, oxygen, and nitrogen. The Tarantula Nebula, 30 Doradus, in the Large Cloud is one of the most extraordinary displays of nebulosity known any-where—in our Galaxy or in others. In Figure 18 it is shown in blue and in red light, and in Figure 21 in red light with three different exposure times. Its total apparent magnitude is approximately 4.0. The corresponding absolute brightness, —15, is therefore greater than that of many of the lesser galaxies in our neighborhood. Many years ago Paraskevopoulos and the writer noted that in the center of the 30 Doradus nebulosity is a cluster of supergiant blue stars.[15] Some of them are doubtless the source of the excitation of the shining nebulosity which spreads out in all directions to a distance of 375 light years. Obscuring nebulosities (dust clouds) that apparently are a part of the total 30 Doradus complex appear to extend to nearly double that distance.

Several other conspicuous or peculiar irregular nebulae appear in the Large Cloud. With practically no exception they are associated with blue supergiant stars, and presumably are in regions of currently rapid stellar evolution. Over the years both stars and nebulosities should be carefully watched to see if evolution is detectable as pro-

13. *Harv. Bul.,* No. 886 (1932). De Vaucouleurs estimates 4,700 stars in the Large Cloud brighter than photographic magnitude 14.0 and about 500 brighter than 14.3 in the Small Cloud (*loc. cit.,* p. 43).

14. Harlow Shapley and Margaret L. Walton, *Harv. Circ.,* No. 288 (1925).

15. *Astroph. Jour., 86,* 340–42 (1937) (Harv. Reprint 141).

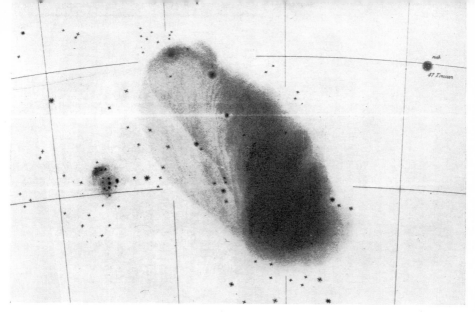

Figure 16 (*above*). The Small Magellanic Cloud. James Dunlop "A Catalogue of Nebulae and Clusters of Stars in the Southern Hemisphere Observed at Paramatta in New South Wales," *Phil. Trans. Roy. Soc., London, 118,* 113–51 (1828)

Figure 17 (*below*). Dunlop's 1828 drawing of the Large Magellanic Cloud

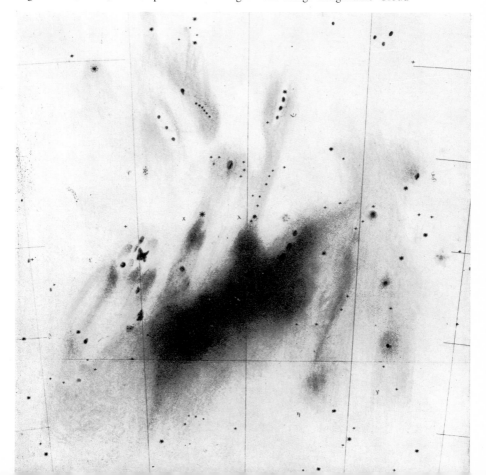

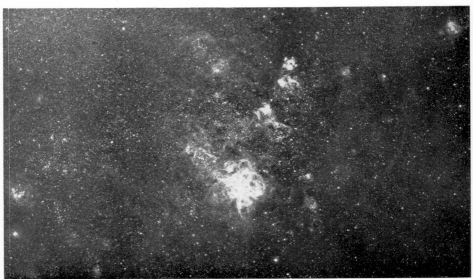

Figure 18. Blue (*above*) and red photographs of 30 Doradus made with the Armagh-Dunsink-Harvard reflector

Figure 19a. The Large and Small Magellanic Clouds on a Harvard sky patrol photograph.

Figure 20. The smooth distribution of stars around the South Galactic Pole. Plate center 1ʰ 20ᵐ, −25°. South at top of figure. (See Ch. 5.)

Figure 19b. The boundaries of the Clouds at 3.5 meters' wave length compared with the hydrogen emission line boundaries. The dark areas represent definite regions of 3.5 meters' radiation and the lighter areas possible regions of the radiation. The dotted lines outline the neutral hydrogen boundaries. *Australian Journal of Science*, 1955.

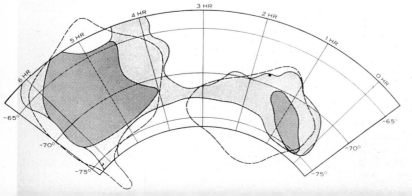

Figure 21.
Photographs of 30
Doradus in red with
the 60-inch reflector.
Exposures of 2, 30,
and 120 minutes

gressive changes of magnitude or spectrum. Recent studies of the spectra and colors of these nebulosities by Harvard, Michigan, and Armagh observers are laying the groundwork for the detailed analyses of the future.[16]

One of the most remarkable nebulae is a great pseudoplanetary, which was at first identified as a ring nebula with a faint central star.[17] But if it is of the same general linear dimensions as the planetary and ring nebulae of our own galactic system, it must be near, must be a member of the foreground. We now believe, however, that the object is a peculiar member of the Large Cloud, a singularly symmetrical H II region (ionized hydrogen) with an over-all diameter of approximately 350 light years.[18] The better photographs show much interior detail. Further spectroscopic work on the nebulosity and enclosed stars, including measures of radial velocities, will soon settle the question.

G. Constellations

We have noted that the large gaseous nebulae are frequently associated with groups of stars, but some of the larger star groups are relatively free of conspicuous nebulosity, bright or dark. The linear dimensions of these stellar aggregations are so great that we cannot equate them with the ordinary galactic clusters of our own system, such as the Pleiades and Praesepe; and in dimensions and stellar characteristics they are quite unlike the globular star clusters. In fact, these oversize stellar organizations much more nearly resemble in stellar content and dimensions the large associations represented by the constellations of Orion, Vela, and Scorpio. We have therefore chosen to call them constellations. A listing of some of the most conspicuous in the large Cloud is taken from Harvard Reprint 373 [1953].

16. For instance, V. M. Nail, C. A. Whitney, and C. M. Wade, *Proc. Nat. Acad. Sci., 39,* 1168–78 (1953) (Harv. Reprint 377); K. G. Henize and F. D. Miller, *Pub. Obs. Mich., 10,* 75 (1951); E. M. Lindsay, *Irish Ast. Jour., 3,* 10 (1954).

17. Jenka Mohr, *Harv. Bul.,* No. 907 (1938). See discussions by C. S. Gum and G. de Vaucouleurs, *The Obs., 73,* 152 (1953); E. M. Lindsay, *Irish Ast. Jour., 2,* 219 (1953).

18. D. S. Evans and A. D. Thackeray, *Mon. Not. Roy. Ast. Soc., 110,* 431 (1950).

The *NGC* number refers to only one of several catalogued groups in each constellation. The linear dimensions of the five aggregates are based on the currently adopted distance modulus of 18.6 (corrected for intervening space absorption). The population data refer to stars brighter than apparent red magnitude 14.0, which corresponds for blue stars to absolute magnitude —4.6. Very few of the stars included in these groups are superposed from our Milky Way; but in some constellations, such as No. V, lying in the Bar of the Cloud, there is doubtless a contribution to the population from the foreground and background parts of the Cloud itself.

| | | | Number of Supergiants | |
| | | *Mean* | | |
No.	*NGC*	*Diameter*	*Blue*	*Red*
I	1935	1,300 l.y.	14	2
II	1966	850	22	2
III	1974	1,400	32	2
IV	1869	1,650	15	2
V	1910	1,200	30	1

Only one object in the Small Cloud can be called a constellation in the sense used for the Large Cloud. It is the aggregate, 1,000 light years in extent, comprising *NGC* 456, 460, and 465. In this constellation, which lies far out in the direction of the Large Cloud, the giant blue stars are enmeshed in nebulosity. A half dozen or more of its bright-line objects have been noted on recent objective prism plates. On a red sensitive emulsion the structure of the aggregate is very irregular.

H. Star clusters

It is difficult to draw a dividing line between field irregularities (star clumpiness) and semiregular open clusters, and between loose open clusters and the compact groups. The difficulty holds for the Magellanic Clouds as well as for our Galaxy. Nevertheless it is possible to sort out three general types of star clusters, all of them much smaller than the constellations and of closer organization than that prevailing among the field irregularities. The three types are globular, circular, and open. Some uncertainty is recognized at the margins of the types, and in all three we are undoubtedly dealing only with the most luminous. Below the 14th magnitude there probably are a few undiscovered clusters of the globular and circular types, and an indefinite number of open systems that resemble the Hyades.

The objects that we would now list as genuine globular clusters on the basis of their integrated spectra, colors, and magnitudes, their apparent smooth structure, and their dimensions appear in the accompanying table.[19] The first three are in the Small Magellanic Cloud; the

NGC	Spectrum (Miss Cannon)	Color (G and K)	Apparent Magnitude	Diameter
121	G5	+0.70	11.4	1′.8
416	K?	0.50	11.8	1.0
419	G	0.54	10.4	2.5
1783	F5:	0.48	10.6	2.2
1806	G:	0.60	11.3	1.4
1835	F8	0.56	10.5	1.2
1846	G5	0.58	11.0	1.3
1856	G:	0.20	9.9	1.4
1978	G	0.64	10.7	2.8
2056	G	...	11.7	1.3

others in the Large Cloud. In two of these (*NGC* 121 and 1978) Thackeray and Wesselink report the finding of variable stars, presumably of the cluster type, at about the 19th magnitude.[20]

Objects which, among others, are circular in outline appear in another table—the first three in the Small Cloud. Some of them look globular, and have even been so listed in earlier publications; but on

NGC	Spectrum	Color	Apparent Magnitude
339	..	0.45	12.3
458	..	0.00	11.4
H.C. 275/3	..	0.22	12.8:
1711	F5	..	9.7
1831	G	0.18	10.65
1866	A3	0.07	9.38
2107	F2	0.25	11.36
2134	A3	0.10	10.76

19. *Proc. Nat. Acad. Sci., 39,* 349–62 (1953) (Harv. Reprint 372) and H. Shapley and V. M. Nail, *Proc. Nat Acad. Sci., 40,* 1–5 (1954) (Harv. Reprint 382).

20. A. D. Thackeray and A. J. Wesselink, *Nature, 171,* 693 (1953); *The Obs., 75,* 33 (1955). Also they find variables in *NGC* 1466, which lies between the Clouds.

the basis of color and spectrum, or sometimes because of internal irregularity, they are now put provisionally in this special category. In our own system, objects such as Messier 11 and *NGC* 2477 would appear circular in outline to a remote external observer, but they are not globular clusters. The use of the word "circular" is not intended to imply that these objects are not spheroidal. Later work may shift some of them to the globular category. In fact, Gerald E. Kron, who has used the Harvard ADH plates in a further examination of the structure and colors, has transferred to the globular class several of the circular clusters. His work is described in a series of reports on clusters in the Magellanic Clouds printed in the *Publications of the Astronomical Society of the Pacific* beginning in 1956; it supplements his earlier measures of colors with Gascoigne (the G and K of the foregoing tables).

The open cluster of the Magellanic Clouds are too numerous to list here; eventually they can be assembled in half a dozen overlapping categories. We suggest the following classification scheme, which does not involve the spectra or colors of member stars:

Loose, irregular aggregations without obvious nebulosity:	I
Loose, irregular aggregations with obvious nebulosity:	I*n*
Symmetrical open groups without obvious nebulosity:	II
Symmetrical open groups with obvious nebulosity:	II*n*
Compact centrally concentrated clusters without nebulosity:	III
Compact centrally concentrated clusters with nebulosity:	III*n*

Examples of these types, chosen from among those with catalogue numbers, are listed here. A number of the open clusters are subdivisions of constellations.

	Small Cloud	*Large Cloud*
I	*IC* 1612	*NGC* 1983
I*n*	*NGC* 456	1858
II	361	2010
II*n*	256	1850
III	294	1866
III*n*	306	1872

Along the Bar of the Large Cloud we have counted 19 open clusters. In nearly all of them blue stars are found among the brightest cluster members. The brightest circular cluster *NGC* 1866 is proved nonglobular in Harvard Reprint, Series II, No. 36 (1951), by its variable star population.

I. Further report on the variable stars

The classical cepheids in the Magellanic Clouds are the top attraction of these galaxies when considered as toolhouses for the study of stellar and galactic structures. Their abundance, variety, physical character-istics, and distribution have been the subject of many of our investi-gations. Five of the thirteen most significant contributions from the Clouds mentioned above concern variable stars, four of them dealing with classical cepheids. In an earlier section of this chapter the history of the discovery of the variables is summarized. A few additional comments will illustrate the usefulness of the variables to past and future workers on the Magellanic Clouds as well as in variable star research.

1. *The total number of various types of variables.* The search for variable stars in the Large Cloud is by no means exhaustive. Perhaps the number with variations greater than two-tenths of a magnitude could be doubled by careful searching, and without going fainter than apparent magnitude 17.5. These would all be giant and supergiant stars. In general the Harvard discoveries are limited to variations in stars brighter than 17.5 with amplitudes greater than four-tenths of a magnitude. With such limits of amplitude and magnitude our survey must be at least three-fourths complete. A table shows for both Clouds the distribution among the various types of the variables that have received Harvard Variable (HV) numbers.

Type	Large Cloud	Small Cloud	Total
Cepheid	550	670	1,220
Nova	5	4	9
Long-period	23	12	35
Irregular	90	27	117
Eclipsing	50	27	77
Cluster	33	11	44
Undetermined	1,381	813	2,194
Total	2,132	1,564	3,696

Among the unworked stars the proportion of the various types is probably much the same as among those whose types have been identified. Making allowance for the stars that should be dropped because of little or no variation, we suggest that the total number of classical cepheids in our census may be something like 1,400 for the Large Cloud, 1,200 for the Small Cloud.

All of the classical cepheids and the novae are physical members of the Clouds. The galactic latitudes of $-33°$ and $-45°$ are too high, and the apparent magnitudes too faint, for galactic system variables of these types to appear in superposition on the Clouds. The same is true for the long-period and irregular variables of the above tabulation, and for most of the eclipsing binaries. How many faint galactic system variables should we expect in the areas of the Clouds? To find the average frequency (number of variables per square degree) for each of these types, we explored thoroughly several variable star fields that are well outside the Clouds but in the same galactic latitudes.[21] In this way we could assure ourselves that below the 14th magnitude, where almost all of these Cloud variables are found, there is no appreciable contribution from the stars of our Galaxy, except for the cluster type variables, of which all 44 are apparently members of our galactic system. Cluster type cepheids that are actual physical members of the Clouds would be fainter than our limit for variables, the 18th magnitude,[22] and this may be true also for the ordinary long-period variables. The long-period and irregular variables that appear in the foregoing tabulation are supergiants, a number of them excessively bright. A few of the 77 eclipsing stars may be superposed variables of the W Urase Majoris type, but most of them certainly are Cloud members.

Unfortunately novae are much less abundant in the Clouds than in the Andromeda Nebula and our Galaxy. Persistent searching on long series of plates has failed to bring out one-tenth as many novae as are found in those two giant Sb spirals. No supernova has been recorded in the Clouds. It is of interest that their recognized ordinary novae all attain to approximately the same absolute magnitude at maximum, between -7 and -8, in rough agreement with the data from the Andromeda Nebula and our Galaxy.

The irregular variables are, as would be expected, most abundant in regions of conspicuous nebulosity. The eclipsing variables for

21. Shapley and Nail, *Proc. Nat. Acad. Sci., 37,* 138–45 (1951) (Harv. Reprint 346).
22. Thackeray and Wesselink, *The Obs., 75,* 33 (1955).

which periods and light curves have been derived include many of the Beta Lyrae subtype with high absolute magnitudes, relatively short periods, and conspicuous secondary minima.[23]

2. The period-luminosity relation. The most striking single characteristic of the cepheids in the Magellanic Clouds is, of course, the high correlation of period length with luminosity. Of increasing importance at the present time are the deviations, that is, the considerable scatter around the mean period-magnitude curves in both Clouds, as well as in localized sections of the Clouds. These deviations have been continuously examined by the Harvard observers, and we have come to the conclusion that the scatter is largely due to the following causes:

a. The unequal light dimming by localized obscuring dust in the Clouds.

b. The thickness of the Clouds; the cepheids on the far edge, for example, could be fainter, and lie below the mean period-magnitude curve, because of their greater distance and also because of the resulting greater contact of their light with the local dust.

c. Inherent scatter in luminosity for a given period [24] (or scatter in period for a given luminosity).

The revision a few years ago of the zero point of the period-luminosity curve, and the effect of the revision on the estimates of distances and dimensions of the Magellanic Clouds, have been fully discussed elsewhere [25] and summarized in the comprehensive paper by Buscombe, Gascoigne, and de Vaucouleurs.[26] They also report on the initiation of color studies, of the cepheids and other supergiant stars, which will become an important part of the new researches on the Clouds. Photoelectric magnitude sequences should soon be available for calibrating the numerous Harvard photographic sequences and extending them to the 20th magnitude. These stabilized magnitude standards should make possible many detailed investigations of the magnitude-color arrays for various sections of the Clouds. Already

23. Shapley and Nail, *Proc. Nat. Acad. Sci., 34,* 173–9 (1948) (Harv. Reprint 306).

24. Wallenquist suggests that the deviating fainter median values in the Harvard lists may refer to "Population II" cepheids (W Virginis type), such as appear in globular clusters. *Uppsala Medd.,* No. 111 (1954).

25. *Proc. Nat. Acad. Sci., 39,* 349–57 (1953) (Harv. Reprint 372).

26. *Supplement to the Aust. Jour. Sci., 17,* No. 3 (1954).

an important study has been made at Columbia University on the colors and magnitudes of supergiant stars brighter than absolute magnitude —4 in the Small Clouds.[27]

Our studies of the classical cepheids in the Clouds have established one definitive result: although highly valuable in sounding the approximate depths of the universe, the period-luminosity relation, because of the considerable scatter, will perhaps always be of low precision in measuring intergalactic distances, except when mean values for scores of variables are available.

3. The period-position relation in the Small Cloud. No satisfactory explanation has yet been advanced to account for the singular fact that in the Small Cloud (less definitely in the Large) the cepheids in the main body have periods on the average more than twice the average period of variables on the borders. There are, to be sure, a few short periods in the nucleus, but such stars are probably superposed from the foreground and background of the Cloud; and there are a few scattered long-period cepheids far from the center (as in the wing, mentioned on an earlier page). However, the situation is as shown in the table.[28]

Location	Number of Variables	Median Period (days)
"Core" of cloud	21	6.47
Intermediate	13	4.70
Borders	78	2.70
All central area	138	4.85
All outer area	157	2.99

One of the following possibilities may account for this remarkable correlation:

a. The larger masses and longer periods may be associated with a high average density of pre-star materials, the abundance of available material permitting rich accretions during the formative stages of the stars. The classical cepheids in the direction of our galactic center also have longer periods than the average for the galactic system, and the periods in globular clusters are similarly long.

b. The equipartition of energy may be responsible for some of the

27. J. Schilt, I. Epstein, and S. J. Hill, *Ast. Jour., 60,* 341 (1955).
28. Shapley and Nail, *Proc. Nat. Acad. Sci., 26,* 105–15 (1940) (Harv. Reprint 192).

observed wider distribution of the shortest-period cepheids in the Small Cloud, since they are presumably less massive than the cepheids of the core and of the main body of the Cloud.

c. In some hypothetical earlier nebulous stage in the development of the Clouds the relative abundance of the chemical elements may have varied from center to edge, and the chemical composition may to some extent control stellar mass and density, and therefore pulsation period. A. R. Hogg has recently found that the color of the Small Cloud is systematically bluer in the brighter central regions than nearer the edge.[29]

4. The standard light curve. Eventually each cepheid may merit individual treatment. But for illustrative and theoretical work there is some value in an accurate accounting of the average behavior—that is, the average of a number large enough to provide statistical significance. From a special photometric study of 89 cepheids in the two Clouds [30] we have derived the mean light-curve coordinates given in the accompanying table for 43 classical cepheids with periods shorter than eight days, and for nineteen with periods longer than ten days.

Coordinates for Mean Light Curves

Phase	Mean Magnitude		Phase	Mean Magnitude	
	Per. $< 8^d 0$	*Per.* $> 10^d 0$		*Per.* $< 8^d 0$	*Per.* $> 10^d 0$
0.00	15.333	14.193	0.50	16.173	15.205
0.05	15.428	14.291	0.55	16.230	15.258
0.10	15.564	14.434	0.60	16.276	15.279
0.15	15.679	14.553	0.65	16.313	15.256
0.20	15.778	14.662	0.70	16.336	15.186
0.25	15.855	14.754	0.75	16.334	15.085
0.30	15.923	14.849	0.80	16.292	14.968
0.35	15.987	14.944	0.85	16.179	14.867
0.40	16.057	15.041	0.90	15.938	14.715
0.45	16.121	15.132	0.95	15.575	14.431

We have omitted the double maxima cepheids with periods around nine days. The individual light curves have been published in the *Harvard Annals*.[31] Standard light curves for galactic cepheids have

29. *Mon. Not. Roy. Ast. Soc., 115,* 473 (1955).
30. *Proc. Am. Phil. Soc., 93,* 40–4 (1948) (Harv. Reprint. Ser. II, 29).
31. Shapley and McKibben, *Harv. Ann., 90,* 253–61 (1940). Shapley, Carlston, and Nail, *Harv. Ann., 109,* 46–56 (1948).

been given by Kukarkin and Parenago on the basis of light curves from various sources.[32] They also used data on cepheids in Messier 31, Messier 33, and *NGC* 6822.

The general dependence of the form of the light curve on period is well illustrated in the Harvard studies, especially by the analysis of the light variations of the 89 variables mentioned above, but at any given place along the sequence of periods different forms of light curve may appear. Not all the variables around the nine-day period, for instance, have double maxima; not all the light curves for periods greater than fifteen days show large amplitudes.

The Magellanic Clouds, which have been more or less continuously photographed since 1890, appear on something like 7,500 plates in the Harvard collection. The long series permits a check on the constancy of the periods and light curves of cepheids. No appreciable changes have been noted in the past half century, but the question has not been thoroughly examined. The time has been too short to reveal easily the changes that eventually must occur.

5. The frequency of periods. Of comparable interest with the dependence of period on distance from the Cloud center is the unusual frequency distribution of periods for the cepheids of the Small Cloud. In the galactic system (where two kinds of cepheids are involved) the median period length is between four and five days. It is much the same for the Large Cloud. In the Small Cloud, however, the mean and median periods are much shorter, and 24 per cent of its cepheids have periods less than two days. In the Large Cloud fewer than 1 per cent of the cepheids so far analyzed have periods less than two days. The anomaly is illustrated in the table.

Period Interval in Days	Percentage of Variables Large	Small
1–2	0.9	23.9
2–3	12.2	21.5
3–4	27.5	15.2
4–5	19.6	8.5
5–10	23.5	16.0
10–20	9.4	9.6
<20	6.9	5.4

32. B. Kukarkin and P. Parenago, *Ast. Jour. Soviet Union, 14,* 181–93 (1937).

It has been suggested that the very short-period classical cepheids of the Small Cloud correspond in some way to the cluster type variables (periods less than a day) in the nucleus of our own Galaxy. However that may be, these stars are unusual and merit further attention.

J. The Magellanic Clouds as galaxies

Ever since we found in 1917 that their distances are greater than 60,000 light years [33] the Clouds have been given status as external systems, or at least as fragments of the Milky Way far from the galactic plane. With the definite identification of spiral and spheroidal "nebulae" as galaxies of stars and nebulosity, the Clouds became recognized as the nearest of all external galaxies—near enough for easy analysis of the supergiant and even the giant stars. Notwithstanding our present acceptance of the Large Cloud as a quasi-barred spiral, both of these nearby systems can best be grouped with the 3 or 4 per cent of catalogued galaxies that we class as irregular. Many of the irregularities exhibited by nonsymmetrical systems are quite different from the seemingly chaotic structure of the Magellanic Clouds. Some pairs of irregular galaxies, however, closely resemble the Magellanic pair, and many of the single irregular galaxies closely resemble one or the other of the Clouds.

In treating the Magellanic Clouds as galaxies two questions naturally arise. Is there some close physical connection of the Clouds with our Milky Way—some connecting stream of stars or nebulosity? That possibility is under investigation by de Vaucouleurs and others. Before the revision of the distance scale we were more inclined to expect a physical connection—the Clouds were thought to be on the outer edge of the Milky Way corona; we even considered them "satellites" of our Galaxy. But current studies show that certainly the Large Cloud and probably both Clouds are considerably above the average in size and mass among the galaxies in our immediate neighborhood. Recent estimates by Kerr and de Vaucouleurs, based on preliminary measures of the velocities of interstellar hydrogen clouds,[34] give provisionally for

33. *Astroph. Jour.*, 48, 155 (1918).
34. Frank J. Kerr and G. de Vaucouleurs, *Aust. Jour. Phys.*, 8, 508–22 (1955). They are exploring the Clouds for 21 cm radiation. Important radio work on the Clouds and bright southern galaxies at wave length 3.5 meters

the Large Cloud a mass of 2.5×10^9 times the solar mass, and for the Small Cloud 1.5×10^9

Although the Large Cloud may be less than a tenth as massive as our own giant Galaxy, it is in turn gigantic compared with a dozen dwarf systems within a distance of two million light years from our Galaxy. Since the separation of the Clouds from the nucleus of the galactic system is now accepted as more than 150,000 light years, we should probably say that they are associated with the Galaxy only in the sense that they are members of the local family—a family that includes also Messier 33, Messier 31 and its two smaller companions, and probably a few other less conspicuous systems. It is not likely that either Cloud has recently passed through the rich star fields of our Milky Way since both are still heavily infused with the interstellar dust that presumably would have been largely cleared away by such a passage.

The most recent analysis of motions in the Magellanic Clouds, as indicated by radio measures of neutral hydrogen, has been summarized by Kerr and de Vaucouleurs as follows;

The radial velocities measured in a survey of the 21 cm line from the Magellanic Clouds are discussed principally in terms of the median velocity for each line profile. It is shown that each cloud is rotating, and the analysis confirms the view, based on optical evidence, that the Clouds are flattened and tilted systems. The gas is probably the least flattened constituent of each Cloud and shows a large decrease of rotational speed with increasing distance from the equatorial plane.

The mean radial velocities of the Large and Small Clouds with respect to the Sun, weighted according to the 21 cm surface brightness, are found to be 280 and 161 km/sec. Other internal motions, both systematic and random, are also indicated by the profiles.

In the sequence of galactic forms the Magellanic-type galaxies appear at one end—at the young end, according to the hypothesis proposed by the writer many years ago.[35] If there is an evolution from one type to another—and that seems to be a natural assumption—the

has just been published, also from Sydney Radiophysics Laboratories, by B. Y. Mills, *Aust. Jour. Phys., 8,* 368–89 (1955), who, in summarizing, reports that "it appears that at wavelength of 3.5 meters the emission from the Magellanic Clouds originates principally in a non-thermal process and has a distribution which is closely related to the interstellar gas and bright stars."

35. For example, *Galaxies,* p. 216 (1943).

developmental trend of a rotating spiral galaxy must be in the sense of disrupting the clusters and the groupings along the spiral arms through shearing, with the result of smoothing out irregularities. Turbulence on a grand scale, von Weizsäcker points out, also tends to transform the spiral and irregular structures in the direction of smooth spheroidal types. Whatever the evolutionary trend, the irregular dust-and-gas-rich Magellanic Clouds appear to possess many characteristics of youth.[36] Perhaps a close watch over a few centuries will reveal that measurable progress has been made in cleaning up the gas and dust, lowering the intensive radiation of the supergiants, and organizing the structures into more symmetrical forms.

36. The youthfulness, however, refers chiefly to the giant stars and the prevalence of much dust and gas, for the presence of many globular clusters suggests an age of perhaps 5 billion years, according to the stellar evolutionary theories developed by Martin Schwarzschild, Allan R. Sandage, and others.

CHAPTER 5. THE SOUTH GALACTIC POLAR ZONE SURVEYS

The metagalactic surveys undertaken at the Harvard Observatory depend on photographs made with cameras that competently cover large areas, while the pioneer surveys of faint galaxies made some years ago at Mount Wilson by Hubble [1] and at the Lick Observatory by Mayall [2] were based on the small-field plates made with conventional reflectors; satisfactory "field flatteners" were not then available. With such plates, except for the central one-fifth of a square degree, substantial corrections to the magnitudes and numbers of galaxies must be applied to allow for the losses through image deformation. The large-field cameras, on the other hand, require no appreciable "distance" corrections over areas 50 to 100 times as large. They do not reach as deep, however, and the reflectors' limitation of field size is compensated by the increase in depth.

Section I. A REVEALING REGION FOR METAGALACTIC EXPLORATION

A. Preliminary on the four polar zones

In the examination of the large-scale distribution of galaxies, both on the surface of the sky and in depth, our best results have been obtained in the galactic polar zones, $\beta > +60°$ and $\beta < -60°$. There are two reasons for this circumstance. The spotty as well as the general space absorption is of little effect in regions so far from the Milky Way, and in fact it can generally be neglected. Secondly, the positions in the sky of these polar zones are satisfactory for observations from both the Boyden and the Agassiz stations. The number of galaxies entering the Harvard work in the north and south galactic polar zones is shown in the table. Included are data for the two celestial polar areas; neither of these is clear of heavy low-latitude absorption, nor do they provide the advantage of zenithal location. The extent of the

1. Edwin Hubble, *Astroph. Jour., 79,* 8–76 (1934). (*Mt. Wilson Contr.,* No. 485).
2. Nicholas U. Mayall, *Lick Bul., 16,* 177–98 (1934).

work on individual galaxies in these four zones has been described briefly in Chapter 2. The first zone is now discussed in some detail, in part as an illustration of procedure but chiefly because in the south galacatic polar zone we deal with one of the most revealing parts of the sky so far as the structure of the Metagalaxy is concerned. Moreover for the Boyden Station the south galactic polar zone is zenithal—a decided advantage for long-exposure photography.

Zone	Area Covered	Telescope	Total of Galaxies Studied
South galactic	β —60° to —90°	Bruce	80,000
North galactic	β +60 to +90	Metcalf and Bruce	95,000
South celestial	δ —60 to —90	Bruce	36,000
North celestial	δ +70 to +90	Metcalf	16,600

B. Errors and oversights

The measuring of the galaxies throughout this zone has aimed at uniformity. Almost without exception the plates have been of good quality with three-hour exposures on fast emulsions (Cramer Hi-Speed or Eastman 103a-0). The search for and marking of the nebular objects has been done by experienced observers using low-power magnifiers. False objects have occasionally been marked, of course, especially where two or more faint stars are so grouped that near the magnitude limit of the plates they simulate the irregular or soft images of galaxies. The testing of various fields by the more penetrating exposures with the 60-inch Rockefeller reflector has not only revealed some mistakes but also shown that we overlook about as many faint galaxies as we falsely record. The statistics of the population are not appreciably affected, therefore, by such errors and oversights. Hubble came to the same conclusion in his galaxy counts, where both mistaken images and oversights average something like 3 or 4 per cent of the total count.

C. The stellar foreground

Photographs made with patrol cameras show a remarkably smooth distribution of stars to the 15th magnitude in the south galactic polar zone. In this region the irregularities in the distribution of the absorbing matter within the galactic system must be very small. Figure 20 shows a section of this polar area, about 400 square degrees, as recorded on patrol plate AX 4309. Recently the Palomar 48-inch Schmidt telescope has recorded some streaks of bright nebulosity in this direction, presumably located not far from the galactic plane and the observer. But neither the nebulosity nor the nonluminous dust associated with it affects appreciably the faint-star distribution or that of the galaxies lying beyond. (A quantitative test of the clarity is reported in Chapter 14.) Moreover, the south galactic polar zone is free of large groups of bright galaxies, such as the Virgo Cloud and its extensions, which dominate the distribution, at least to the 15th magnitude, in the north galactic polar zone. The southern zone is accordingly the most suitable region for examination of the general distribution of average galaxies to magnitude 17.5, that is, to a distance of the order of 150 million light years.

D. Conspicuous objects

Several objects of special interest are within this polar zone, which covers 2,760 square degrees, or one-fifteenth of the entire sky. It contains the large spirals *NGC* 247 and *NGC* 908, the high-latitude globular clusters *NGC* 288 and 7492, and the giant (in angular size) planetary nebula *NGC* 7293. Some of these appear in Figure 20.

Also we find in this zone the dwarf spheroidal galaxies, called the Sculptor and Fornax superclusters, the discovery of which on Harvard patrol plates in 1938–39 first brought to our attention the type of faint galaxy that may be the most common of all extragalactic systems. They also have been studied at the Mount Wilson and Pretoria (Radcliffe) observatories, and will appear again in our consideration of the local family of galaxies (Chapter 9). In this polar zone a number of relatively bright spheroidal and spiral galaxies are grouped in the constellation of Fornax. They appear to form a sparse physical system and illustrate the fact that some of the spheroidal galaxies are supergiants, exceeding in luminosity most of the giant spirals.

The Shapley-Ames catalogue lists here 94 galaxies brighter than apparent magnitude 12.9 (revised). The Dreyer catalogues *NGC* and *IC* record 769 objects, mostly galaxies. The remainder of the 89,000 galaxies discussed below for this area of 2,760 square degrees were first marked on the Harvard plates. There would probably be about twenty million in the zone brighter than the 22d magnitude.

We are now ready to proceed with the two major discussions of galaxies in the south galactic polar zone, the first dealing with the galaxy counts without differentiation as to brightness or distance, the second based on magnitude measures for about 40 per cent of the recorded galaxies.

Section II. SURVEY BASED ON THE DISTRIBUTION
OF 80,000 GALAXIES

E. *Observational material*

The photography involves 80 long-exposure plates (Series A) made with the Bruce telescope at the Boyden Station. The centers of 71 of them fall within the polar area bounded by β —60°; the others in the interval β —55° to —60°. Altogether 89,352 galaxies have been marked, of which about 8,000 are outside the β —60° boundary. The objects occasionally doubly counted, because of plate overlap, are much less numerous than the unrecorded objects in the gaps between the plate edges. Each plate covers approximately 35 square degrees, and with allowance for overlap some 80 per cent of the whole polar region has been photographed on the long-exposure plates. With A plates of shorter exposure, and plates of other series, the whole zone is completely and many times covered for objects of the 15th magnitude and brighter.

Near the edges of the Bruce plates there is a distinct loss in magnitude, and a corresponding loss in number of discoverable galaxies, because of vignetting and image distortion. The central nine square degrees of each plate, however, show no appreciable magnitude and number loss and yield an average of approximately $\bar{N}_9 = 50$ galaxies per square degree. In the surrounding sixteen square degrees there are only $\bar{N}_{16} = 31$ objects per square degree. This decrease indicates an average loss in limiting magnitude, compared with the plate centers, of $\Delta m = 1.67 \log (\bar{N}_9/\bar{N}_{16}) = 0.35$ (we must assume for this and similar calculations a roughly uniform distribution of galaxies in depth). Outside the central $9 + 16 = 25$ square degrees, the loss in magnitude limit and number is much greater (about 0.8 magnitudes, compared with the plate centers) and the data from these peripheral regions therefore have little value.

F. *Census by way of galaxy counts*

In the first discussion of this area we shall consider the total numbers of galaxies after the reduction of these numbers to a common limiting magnitude. Since this is the most important and laborious of the special surveys carried through at the Harvard Observatory, more space is given to the description of methods and results than for other areas reported in later chapters.[3]

Table 5 illustrates the material for ten plates and gives the totals and means for all 80 plates.[4] The galactic coordinates are computed on the basis of the conventional pole.[5] The indication of plate quality in the second column is the mean of estimates by two observers.[6] The highest qualities 8, 9, and 10 are seldom attained, and low-quality plates 1, 2, and 3 have been used as little as possible.

Table 5. Population Data for South Galactic Polar Zone

Plate	Q	$N\,Pub.$	$N\,Tot.$	N_9	m_s	$\bar{N}_r$
18691	7	63	4,519	1,730	19.4	48.1
16149	4	23	382	157	18.5	15.2
17231	6	5	2,208	784	18.0	151.6
17946	5	12	2,010	853	18.0	164.9
17971	6	9	1,927	1,012	18.9	56.2
15790	4	6	385	212	18.6	17.9
14871	3	10	547	205	18.2	30.1
15802	7	61	684	274	18.9	15.2
14860	4	8	666	235	18.3	30.0
14992	5	6	1,043	422	18.3	54.0
Totals and means for 80 plates	5.4	2,152	89,352	36,274	18.36	51.51

The fourth, fifth, and seventh columns of the table give for each plate the total number of galaxies, the number in the central nine square degrees, and the average number per square degree in the central nine-square after reduction to a common limiting magnitude. The

3. Many members of the Observatory staff have assisted in the details of the research on the south galactic polar zone. J. S. Paraskevopoulos and his associates at the Boyden Station provided the plate material. R. E. Rogers, W. P. Neumann, and Virginia McKibben Nail made the star counts upon which the magnitudes have been based. The marking of the faint galaxies and the identifications of known systems were the work of Mrs. S. F. M. Lindsay and Miss Constance D. Boyd, who also assisted in the calculations and the preparing of tabulations.

4. The full tabulation, including positions in equatorial and galactic coordinates for the centers of the 80 individual plates, is printed in *Harv. Circ.,* No. 423 (1937)

5. J. Ohlsson, *Ann. Lund Obs.,* No. 3 (1932).

6. C. D. Boyd and H. Shapley; see *Harv. Circ.,* No. 423 (1937).

number of objects heretofore published is shown in the third column.

The limiting magnitude for stars, m_s, determined from star counts and given in the sixth column of Table 5, refers to the image of a particular star which though very faint can still be clearly observed. (Actually the plates record objects two- or three-tenths of a magnitude fainter than m_s.) To determine this limit, an area of two square degrees was counted on each plate by two different observers. The counts were reduced with the Seares and van Rhijn tables,[7] which interrelate magnitudes, star numbers, and galactic coordinates. For declinations south of $-23°$ the van Rhijn tables alone were used. The average m_s is 18.38 and 18.34 for plates north and south of declination $=$ $-23°$, respectively. The latitude of the Boyden Station, where practically all of these plates were made, is $-29°$, and therefore the zenith distances were reasonably small for all plates. It follows that the near identity of the two values of m_s above can be taken as evidence of a comfortable consistency in the magnitude standards.

G. Reduction of galaxy counts to a common limit

Since the quality of the plates varies and their effectiveness in recording stars and galaxies depends upon sky conditions, speed of emulsion, plate fog, and possibly other factors, the limiting magnitude differs from plate to plate both for stars and for galaxies. If the limiting stellar magnitude, m_s, is used as an indicator of plate speed and effectiveness, the number of galaxies observed on each plate can be reduced to the number that would be found at a chosen common stellar magnitude limit m_0 through application of a reduction factor

$$f = 10^{0.6(m_0 - m_s)},$$

which assumes for each region an essentially uniform space distribution of galaxies along the line of sight. The assumption is admittedly approximate, though necessary at the present time; it can be dropped when and wherever the magnitudes of the individual objects become available. The dispersion of observed values of m_s about the mean is so small that whatever deviations there may be from uniformity do not seriously affect the census in this polar area where we are appar-

7. F. H. Seares and Mary C. Joyner, *Astroph. Jour., 67,* 24–82 (1928) (*Mt. Wilson Contr.,* No. 346); P. J. van Rhijn, *Groningen Pub.,* No. 43 (1929).

ently not working through or into a metagalactic cloud of galaxies.

For the 80 plates employed in this census the mean magnitude limit for stars, which we shall adopt for m_0, is

$$m_s = 18.36 \pm 0.04 \text{ (m.e.)},$$

and it is not altered by the exclusion of the six earliest plates referred to below.

In an earlier detailed study [8] of 87 long-exposure Bruce plates covering the south *celestial* polar zone, declination $< -60°$, and involving measures of individual galaxy magnitudes, we found that the limit of completeness of the survey for faint galaxies, m_n, is on the average a few tenths of a magnitude brighter than m_s; but the difference $m_s - m_n$ is larger and more erratic for plates made before 1930 than for subsequent emulsions. For sixteen plates made prior to 1930, $m_s - m_n = 0.78 \pm 0.09$ (m.e.), with an average deviation of 0.26; but for those made after 1930 the mean magnitude difference is 0.23 ± 0.02 (m.e.), with an average deviation for a single plate of only 0.09. (This small dispersion for the difference $m_s - m_n$ on the later Cramer Hi-Speed plates indicates a useful uniformity in the emulsions.)

To make the present survey as homogeneous as possible we reduced separately the six plates made prior to 1930. The magnitudes of all the galaxies were measured on them, and values of m_n were directly established for each plate from its magnitude-frequency diagram; [9] $m_s - m_n$ was found in the mean to be 0.62 ± 0.08 (m.e.), agreeing well enough with the earlier experience.

For the 74 plates of the south galactic polar zone for which magnitude-frequency curves were not available, the value of $m_s - m_n = 0.23$ was adopted on the basis of the afore-mentioned results from the contemporary plates of the south celestial polar zone.

For the last column of Table 5 the numbers $\bar{N}_r$ of galaxies per square degree on each plate were obtained from N_9 of the fifth column by use of the formulae

$$f = 10^{0.6(m_0 - m_s)}$$
$$\bar{N}_r = fN_9 \div 9$$

8. *Harv. Ann.*, *105*, No. 8 (1937).

9. Some magnitude-frequency diagrams for galaxies in this zone are shown in Figure 23.

and the rounded-off values $m_0 = 18.8$ and $m_0 = 18.4$, respectively, for the early and late plates.

H. A final statistic

The numbers $\bar{N}_r$ refer to the galaxies per square degree to magnitude 18.2. On the average plate there are undoubtedly some undiscovered nebulous objects between magnitudes 18.0 and 18.2, but the partial marking of objects between 18^m2 and m_s (fainter, that is, than the peak of the magnitude-frequency curve) is enough to ensure effective completeness to magnitude 18.2.

When reduced to this common limit, 18.2, the mean of the mean numbers of galaxies per square degree, derived for 720 square degrees on 80 plates, is found to be

$$\bar{N} = \text{Mean of } \bar{N}_r = 51.51 \pm 3.11 \text{ (m.e.).}$$

For the 71 plates within the boundary $\beta -60°$, we find $\bar{N}_r = 50.2$. Before the reduction to the common magnitude limit, these quantities were 50.4 and 52.1, respectively; there has been, therefore, no appreciable enrichment or diminution of the data through the process of introducing homogeneity.

I. Graphical illustration of the census

The distribution of galaxies to magnitude 18.2 is shown in detail on the polar chart in Figure 22. Each plate is represented by a circular area of 25 square degrees. The shading is based on $\bar{N}_r$, the population for the central nine square degrees.

The values of $\bar{N}_r$ range from 15 to 165; and the ten richest regions have 6.2 times the population of the ten poorest. The northwest quadrant of the zone (longitude 0° to 90°) is much poorer than the other quadrants. The mean values are

Quadrant	1	2	3	4
$\bar{N}_r$	31.8	54.2	66.5	51.1
Number of Plates	18	18	21	23

The third quadrant, 180° to 270°, touches at latitude —60° the large metagalactic cloud that appears to extend some 60° to the southeastward, passing the Large Magellanic Cloud and approaching the south celestial pole (see Chapters 4, 7, and 9).

J. The latitude effect

If in the south galactic polar zone a latitude effect on the population of galaxies exists, arising from a uniform layer of absorbing material parallel to and near the galactic plane, it should be in the sense of slightly increasing the population with approach to the galactic pole. But in this zone the observed change is in the opposite direction, the average number increasing with distance from the pole. The result was foreshadowed in an earlier survey of the frequency of galaxies

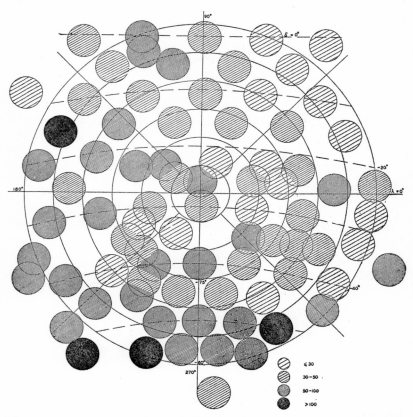

Figure 22. Polar chart showing distribution of southern galaxies to magnitude 18.2

in selected regions throughout all galactic latitudes.[10] The material then used overlaps the present material very little, but we then also found a measurable *decrease* in nebular density from β —55° to the south galactic pole. There may be of course some latitude effect; it seems inevitable. But it can easily be veiled by the inherent irregularities of galaxy distribution.

K. *Computation of the space-density parameter*

The mean value of $\bar{N}_r$ from the 80 plates is of importance in considering the space frequency of galaxies at all measurable distances from the observer. The number 51.5 is based upon the census of 36,274 galaxies in a region of the sky that is, as we have indicated above, apparently clear both of significant galactic space absorption and of conspicuous clustering of stars or galaxies. It seems unlikely that the value $\bar{m}_n = 18.2$ can be in error by more than 0.05. A large number of magnitude sequences based on many selected areas were used in determining this limiting brightness, and the plates after standardization are effectively of uniform quality.

If we adopt tentatively the hypothesis of uniform space frequency of galaxies, we may define a fundamental constant of the Metagalaxy, m_1, as the apparent photographic magnitude to which a survey must extend (in high latitudes) to find on the average one galaxy per square degree. A determination of this parameter, based on more material than has hitherto been available, is now possible with our galaxy counts in the south galactic polar zone. We have

$$m_1 = \bar{m}_n - \delta m - 1.667 \log \bar{N}_r,$$

where $\bar{m}_n$ is the mean magnitude limit for galaxies observed and δm the magnitude correction for red shift. This correction is not large at the 18th magnitude and can be taken, from Hubble's table,[11] as 0.15. We derive from the observed mean values of $\bar{N}_r$ and m_n

$$m_1 = 15.20,$$

which carries with it the same uncertainty as that affecting the observed value of $\bar{m}_n$. Hubble's most recent determination of the con-

10. *Proc. Nat. Acad. Sci., 19,* 389–93 (1933) (Harv. Reprint 90). See diagram and discussion in Chapter 8 below.

11. Edwin Hubble, *Astroph. Jour., 79,* 8–76 (1934) (*Mt. Wilson Contr.,* No. 485).

stant,[12] $m_1 = 15.09$, indicates a slightly higher average space density, but the result is based on samples to fainter limits in both hemispheres, and involves also his smooth correction for absorption as a function of latitude. If we apply to the Harvard result the same correction for latitude, we obtain $m_1 = 15.17$.

My value of m_1 is also in satisfactory agreement with Mayall's [13] determination at the Lick Observatory, 15.3, and Hubble's earlier result, 15.2. But there is a more serious uncertainty in m_1 than the uncertainty in $\bar{m}_n$: the value of $\bar{N}_r$ varies systematically from place to place, and m_1 varies similarly. If we compute m_1 separately for the four quadrants of the south galactic polar zone we find values ranging from 15.00 to 15.54. The adopted value, $m_1 = 15.2$, is, in view of this spread, decidedly an average value. Incidentally, it means that if the sky were everywhere clear of space absorption and if the south galactic polar zone is taken as typical at the 18th magnitude for the whole sky, there are about 40,000 galaxies brighter than magnitude 15.2. Because of the low-latitude space absorption, only about 25,000 can be photographed above the magnitude limit.

L. The spacing of galaxies

The volume of space that must be covered on the average to find one galaxy per square degree brighter than magnitude 15.2 is readily computed. If we take $M = -15.8$ as the absolute magnitude of a typical bright galaxy of apparent magnitude $m = 15.2$, its modulus, $m - M = 31.0$, corresponds to a distance of about 50 million light years. The volume of the one-square-degree cone therefore is approximately 14 cubic m.l.y. Such bright galaxies would on the average be about 2.4 m.l.y. apart.

But the average galaxy in absolute magnitude is nearer -13.8 because of the abundance of dwarfs, and consequently the distance corresponding to $m = 15.2$ is only 40 per cent of that for the galaxies of absolute magnitude -15.8, and the volume is only 0.9 cubic m.l.y. The galaxies, therefore, except when in clusters, are on the average according to this calculation about a million light years apart, and

12. *Astroph. Jour.*, *84*, 517–54 (1936) (*Mt. Wilson Contr.*, No. 557).
13. Nicholas U. Mayall, *Lick Bul.*, *16*, 197 (1934).

there should be about fifteen field galaxies within 1.5 m.l.y. of our galaxy.

Section III. SURVEY BASED ON THE MAGNITUDES OF 31,000 GALAXIES

M. Introduction on depth surveys

The distribution of galaxies on the surface of the sky is easily examined on any uniform collection of long-exposure photographs. An effective study, however, of the distribution in the line of sight requires much greater labor. It is complicated by the difficulties of nebular photometry as well as by uncertainties introduced through the considerable dispersion in the intrinsic luminosities of galaxies. Systems side by side in space can differ by five or more magnitudes in apparent brightness, as for example the Andromeda Nebula and its companions; and a pair with equal apparent brightness may differ in distance by a factor of ten. An exploration in depth, where the linear distances or the absolute magnitudes of individual galaxies are not known, can therefore be only of a statistical nature; but if we assume—and it is reasonable—that the frequencies of the various absolute magnitudes are closely similar from one region to another, we can obtain reliable information on the population density as a function of distance.

In the study of the radial distribution of population it is necessary to use photometric methods for estimating distances, relative or absolute. Except for the few galaxies in our immediate neighborhood where some of the individual stars can be isolated, the apparent magnitude of each galaxy must be measured as a whole. We must determine these total (integrated) magnitudes as accurately as possible, adopt reasonable values of the intervening space absorption and of the mean absolute magnitude, and, in order to diminish the effects of statistical fluctuations, we should survey large areas.

N. The observational material

Approximately 31,000 galaxies on 22 Bruce plates have been measured for the determination of the magnitudes that are summarized in Table 6. All the fields lie in galactic latitudes between —55° and the south galactic pole. Because of the possibly poor magnitude standards south of declination $-23°$, only plates in the northern part of the zone were used for the magnitude study.[14] In this area both the van Rhijn and the Seares and Joyner tables have been employed in setting up the stellar magnitude sequences. Although the photographic magnitude scale is not dependable fainter than magnitude 17.5, down to that magnitude it has the security of being based not only on star counts but also directly on the Mount Wilson magnitudes in the Selected Area Sequences at declinations $-15°$ and $0°$.

In Table 6 the 22 plates are listed in order of right ascension.[15] The second column indicates the quality based on suitability for locating and measuring nebulous objects. Quality 10 represents nonexistent perfection. The fourth column gives the apparent magnitude, m_n, to which the galaxy survey is judged to be complete. The values chosen for m_n are approximate and not of direct significance in this particular study. The average difference between the two limiting magnitudes, and its mean error, are

$$\overline{m_s - m_n} = 0.42 \pm 0.06 \text{ (m.e.)}.$$

This mean value differs from that given in Section I of this chapter, 0.23; some of the limiting magnitudes m_s have been redetermined closer to the plate limits, and m_n is now based directly on observed frequency plots of the nebular magnitudes. The two values are not inconsistent. Several of the plates of Table 6 were specially made for this photometric study and all are of good quality.

The last two columns of Table 6 give the total number of galaxies in the central 25 square degrees and the total for the central nine square degrees where distance corrections can be ignored and where there is diminished likelihood of error of misidentification because of optically deformed images. The grand total for the 25 square de-

14. More than 20 individuals have taken part in the investigations here reported. The marking of the galaxies on the Bruce plates was done chiefly by Sylvia Lindsay, Constance D. Boyd, and Frances W. Wright. Miss Boyd and Miss Wright independently estimated the magnitudes. Robert Porter and Edith Jones made many of the star counts for the establishment of the magnitude sequences. Martha Dowse assisted throughout with calculations and editorial details. The Bruce plates were made by J. S. Paraskevopoulos and his assistants at the Boyden Station.

15. The positions of the plate centers in equatorial and galactic coordinates are given in Table I, *Proc. Nat. Acad. Sci., 26,* 168 (1940) (Harv. Reprint 194).

grees includes about one hundred objects that are twice counted through overlapping.[16]

O. Discussion of the census

The magnitudes, in intervals of a tenth, are assembled in Appendix A for each plate of Table 6. This tabulation of the magnitudes of more than 13,500 galaxies in nearly 200 square degrees of the sky provides

Table 6. Summary of Plates and Counts

Plate	Quality	m_s	m_n	N_{25}	N_9
A 20280	6	18.4	17.7	1,031	340
20318	8	18.3	17.9	1,867	729
17182	6	18.6	18.3	677	295
15781	5	18.0	17.5	546	233
17777	5	18.6	18.5	1,177	537
20484	8	19.6	18.5	1,441	741
20341	8	18.7	18.3	2,078	811
19788	5	18.2	18.0	1,138	448
20347	7	18.4	18.2	2,457	988
17867	7	18.9	18.8	1,601	769
20503	5	18.9	18.2	1,538	686
17084	6	18.2	17.7	664	308
16253	7	18.5	18.1	1,247	588
18691	7	19.3	18.8	3,847	1,341
16213	6	18.4	18.1	740	293
18706	5	18.3	17.6	854	391
18809	6	17.9	17.8	575	230
15814	5	18.4	18.0	781	299
20440	8	18.4	17.8	1,547	796
17946	5	18.1	17.8	1,711	839
20433	7	18.2	17.9	1,997	905
17971	6	18.9	18.6	1,839	951
Means and totals	6.2	18.5	18.1	31,353	13,518

the strongest quantitative evidence we have, up to this time, of the considerable nonuniformity in metagalactic population, as well as a measure of the degree of the nonuniformity.

16. As a result of further measurement and analysis, some of the plates of Table 6 appear in the earlier tabulation with totals and magnitude limits differing somewhat from the present values.

The distances involved for five of the plates reach to a billion light years for galaxies of the luminosity of our own and the Andromeda Nebula; and over the whole area of the south galactic polar zone our survey extends considerably deeper than the bounds of what we have chosen to call the Inner Metagalaxy.

Although the magnitudes of all objects in the central 25 square degrees have been measured, only the homogeneous data for the nine central square degrees on each plate are given in Appendix A and used for the present magnitude-frequency discussion; at the bottom of the table are totals and subtotals.

The plates are not equally potent; some penetrate to nearly twice the depth reached by others, as indicated by the values of m_s and m_n in Table 6. The diversity in the distribution of magnitudes is illustrated in Figure 23 by the data from three plates. (Similar diversity is sometimes manifest on a single plate.)

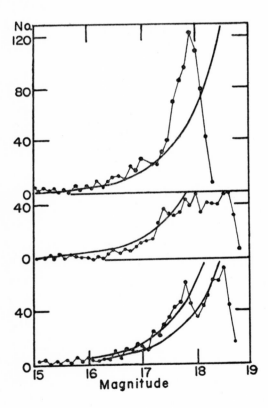

Figure 23. Frequency of magnitudes on plates A 20433 (top), 20503, and 20341. Ordinates are numbers in tenth-of-a-magnitude intervals.

Plate A 20433 is rich, and down to magnitude 17.5 the frequency fits fairly well the theoretical uniform-density curve

$$\log \bar{N} = b(m - m_1) \tag{1}$$

for $m_1 = 15.2$, $b = 0.6$, which are the average values for this zone. But apparently a cloud of galaxies is encountered at about magnitude 17.5, doubling the "uniform" number at magnitude 17.8. (A large error in the magnitude scale, appearing abruptly at magnitude 17.4, could also account for the deviation, but it is improbable.)

In contrast to the foregoing, plate A 20503 is poor, and reaches the uniform-density curve only at 17.3 to 17.5; it then shows the space density falling off sharply with distance until the approaching plate limit disturbs the census at about magnitude 18.5.

Plate A 20341 is somewhat better represented by the lower of the two plotted uniform curves which assumes $m_1 = 15.5$. A clustering of about 150 galaxies appears around $m = 17.5$ at a distance of

$$r = 10^{0.2(17.5+16.5)-4.5}$$
$$\doteqdot 200 \text{ million light years.}$$

For all three diagrams the numbers for nine square degrees in successive tenth-of-a-magnitude intervals are taken directly from Appendix A and are not corrected for red shift. Comparable frequency curves for the other 19 plates can be made from the tabulated data.

P. Derivation of metagalactic parameters

We have shown the nonuniformity in the distribution in depth from plate to plate. Now we shall obtain mean values for the space-density parameter m_1 and the radial density coefficient b.

All the data of Appendix A (22 plates) are represented by a single logarithmic plot in Figure 24. The ordinates are logarithms of the *total* numbers of galaxies brighter than the corresponding magnitudes (abscissae). Before this and subsequent graphs were made, and all the following tabulations, the magnitudes were corrected for the red shift as deduced by Hubble. It is not large for average objects at the distances here concerned, being 0.10 at magnitude 17, 0.15 at magnitude 18, and 0.18 at magnitude 18.5. But if we assume uniform density of matter in space (when averaged over large volumes), the necessity of making these corrections for the red shift can be demonstrated, as in the next paragraph, for without them the deduced coefficient b would differ measurably from the value 0.6.

The straight line that best represents the total material N_t from 198 square degrees, as plotted in Figure 24, is represented by

$$\log N_t = 0.600m - 6.806$$
$$\pm\, 0.011 \quad \pm\, 0.017, \tag{2}$$

where the mean errors are computed from a least squares solution. That the coefficient of m should be exactly 0.6, the value for uniform space density, is of course fortuitous; but the fact that such a large amount of photometric material would yield a density gradient coefficient of this order of magnitude is of basic significance in the exploration of the Metagalaxy. For here we have evidence that we are neither

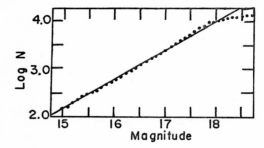

Figure 24. Magnitude frequency for all plates. Abscissae are photographic magnitudes corrected for the red shift; ordinates are logarithms of the cumulative totals. The straight line is defined by Equation (2).

approaching a metagalactic nucleus nor finding an indication of a boundary to the sidereal universe as we go out several hundred million light years in the direction of the south galactic pole.

From equation (1), after reducing the result in equation (2) to one square degree by the relation

$$\log \bar{N} = \log N_t - \log 198 = 0.600m - 9.102,$$

we derive the space-density parameter

$$m_1 = 15.17 \pm 0.03 \quad \text{(m.e.)}. \tag{3}$$

Equation (2) would require, for the area covered by the present survey, eight galaxies brighter than 12.9. An examination of the Shapley-Ames catalogue [17] shows only three systems for the areas covered by the central nine square degrees of these 22 plates. They are

17. *Harv. Ann., 88,* No. 2 (1932).

NGC 175 12^m8
247   10.7
908   11.1

The relatively small population of bright galaxies in the southern galactic hemisphere has been generally recognized and is graphically shown above in Chapter 3.

The foregoing investigation of the magnitude-frequency relation is valid only to a magnitude slightly brighter than 18 because some of the plates are inadequate at that point. The work can be carried to fainter magnitudes than are involved in the derivation of equation (2) by including in the totals and graphs only the data from plates with

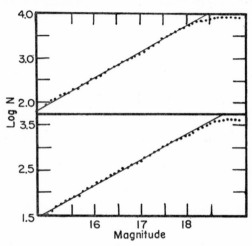

Figure 25. Magnitude frequency for thirteen plates (above) and five plates. Coordinates as in Figure 24. The straight lines are defined by Equations (4) and (5).

fainter magnitude limits. We thus have in Figure 25 two graphs referring to 117 (above) and to 45 square degrees, and representing essentially complete surveys for objects as faint as magnitudes 18.2 and 18.6 respectively. The corresponding linear solutions are

$$\log\ N_{117} = 0.589m - 6.871$$
$$\pm 0.006 \quad \pm 0.009, \tag{4}$$

$$\log N_{45} = 0.571m - 6.981$$
$$\pm 0.006 \quad \pm 0.012, \tag{5}$$

which yield the values

$$m_1 = 15.18 \pm 0.015, \tag{6}$$
$$m_1 = 15.12 \pm 0.02. \tag{7}$$

Giving weights 3, 2, 1, respectively, to the three determinations each of b and m_1 in equations (2) to (7), we obtain the mean results

$$\bar{b} = 0.592 \pm 0.009 \text{ (m.e.)}, \tag{8}$$
$$\bar{m}_1 = 15.16 \pm 0.2 \text{ (m.e.)}. \tag{9}$$

The best representation of the magnitude-frequency plots for individual plates cannot be obtained by linear formulae. The considerable deviations from uniformity in space density, already shown by the plots in Figure 23, and the frequencies in Appendix A, can be further illustrated by calculating the constants, b and m_1, for individual plates. Assembling the material in order of increasing right ascension into three groups of seven plates each,[18] we obtain the following values and mean errors for the two parameters:

	I	*II*	*III*
$\bar{b} =$	0.632	0.571	0.611
	$\pm$ 0.024	$\pm$ 0.009	$\pm$ 0.020
$\bar{m}_1 =$	15.43	15.06	15.09
	$\pm$ 0.05	$\pm$ 0.02	$\pm$ 0.05

From the values of $\bar{m}_1$ it is seen that the population density is conspicuously higher for the greater right ascensions. This result reflects the conspicuous transverse density gradient discussed in a later chapter. A decrease of 0.35 in the parameter corresponds to an increase of about 60 per cent in the space density.

Q. Summary of magnitude analysis

1. The photographic magnitudes of somewhat more than 36,000 galaxies have been twice estimated on 22 Bruce plates, each of three hours' exposure, on fields in the south galactic polar zone ($\beta <$ −60°).

2. The magnitude system for the galaxies is based on that provided for stars through the international standards in Selected Areas; the sequences have been set up by the star-count method and checked by direct reference to Selected Area magnitudes.

3. The high-latitude areas covered by this study are free of serious

18. Plate A 18691 is omitted; its galaxy counts had to be somewhat corrected because of the presence in the field of the dispersed Sculptor cluster, a galaxy.

inequalities in space absorption, if we judge by the distribution of the faint stars. Probably the total dimming of light by interstellar or inter-galactic absorption does not here exceed a quarter of a magnitude.

4. In the summaries of magnitudes in Appendix A, and in the fre-quency curves of Figure 23, we have numerical and graphical illustra-tions, for this favorably explored region, of the deviations from uni-formity in the space distribution of galaxies.

5. Figures 24 and 25 represent what is probably the best informa-tion now available on the average magnitude frequency of galaxies in absorption-free non-cluster regions. A good determination of the space-density parameter is therefore possible for this section of metagalactic space, and the value

$$m_1 = 15.16 \pm 0.02 \text{ (m.e.)}$$

is derived from a discussion of all the data. But values of m_1 differing from this average by much more than the observational error can be obtained if the polar zone is suitably subdivided.

6. From such subdivision, evidence is again found of the strong *transverse* metagalactic density gradient across the south galactic zone; but in the line of sight, when all plates are considered together (13,518 galaxies), the average change of density with distance does not ex-ceed the error of measurement. The adopted mean value of the line-of-sight gradient is

$$b = 0.592 \pm 0.009 \text{ (m.e.)}.$$

7. We have in the present result, with $b = 0.6$ almost exactly, an indication of the necessity of a red-shift correction to the photographic magnitudes fainter than 17.0. Of more importance, we have an inti-mation of the relatively high accuracy (for this area) of the stellar and nebular magnitude scales between magnitudes 15 and 17.5, since a systematic error in the scale as large as 5 per cent is not possible in the mean curves of Figures 24 and 25, unless it chances to be almost exactly balanced by an unrevealed radial density gradient.

8. Our probe to a depth of several hundred million light years yields no indication that we have approached a center or edge of the Metagalaxy.

9. The evaluation of the space-density parameter leads to the esti-mate that on the average galaxies of the general field are separated

by distances of one million light years. We should find, therefore, within 1.5 million light years of our Galaxy about 15 field galaxies, mostly dwarfs. This is close to our present record, and suggests that the "local family" is a group of not more than eight or ten galaxies, embedded in the continuous metagalactic field.

CHAPTER 6. THE NORTH GALACTIC
POLAR ZONE SURVEY

The most inviting area of the sky for future researches on the structure
and behavior of clusters and clouds of galaxies, and on the structure
of the Metagalaxy as a whole, is the area here called the north galactic
polar zone. Four factors contribute to its importance: the presence
of the relatively nearby Virgo Cloud of galaxies, the freedom from
serious space absorption, the richness in assemblages of faint galaxies,
and the zone's convenient location for all the telescopes of both hemispheres. The work at the Harvard Observatory on this region has been
mainly confined in the past to measures of the diameters and magnitudes of the several hundred brightest galaxies found within the zone,
and to one limited deeper probe in the Virgo region, undertaken to
sample space in that direction and if possible find the fainter members
of the Virgo Cloud.

More recently we have completed a general survey to magnitude
17.5 for the whole area from galactic latitude β +60° to β +90°. In
this chapter we summarize the results. The methods employed in the
survey have been described in the preceding chapter. For the most
part the deductions from this census simply confirm and strengthen
what has already been learned from the south galactic polar zone.

A. Population in the polar zone

The galaxy counts summarized in Appendix B were made on two
series of plates, all of three-hour exposures. The 57 A plates, made
with the Bruce telescope in South Africa, show stars to magnitude
18.2 on the average; the star limit for 69 MC plates, made at the
Agassiz Station with the Metcalf doublet, averages magnitude 17.9.
In declination the north galactic polar zone extends from −2° to
+58°. We used the MC instrument for regions north of declination
+22°. The area south of +22° (about 40 per cent of the zone) was
covered with the southern telescope.[1]

Earlier investigations with these instruments had shown that the

1. Except for MC 33360 at decl. + 19°.4. *Proc. Nat. Acad. Sci., 37,* 191–6
(1951) (Harv. Reprint 347).

average-galaxy "completeness" limit m_n is 0.4 magnitude brighter than the star limit m_s for the A plates,[2] and 0.57 magnitude brighter for MC plates.[3] These are average values. The difference $m_s - m_n$ varies from plate to plate because of slightly varying conditions of seeing and focus. The survey therefore lacks uniformity because of this spread, and also because of the residual uncertainties in the magnitude sequences which are based as usual on the Seares and van Rhijn star-count tables.

In order to obtain as uniform a picture of the density distribution as possible for galaxies to magnitude 17.5, we have reduced the galaxy counts on each plate to a common magnitude limit by the application of the factor

$$f = 10^{0.6(18.07 - m_s)}$$

for the MC plates and

$$f = 10^{0.6(17.9 - m_s)}$$

for the A plates, where m_s, in the fifth column of Appendix B, is the observed stellar magnitude limit. It follows that $fN_9 = N_{9r}$, where N_9 is the total number of galaxies found on each plate in a central area 3° on a side, and N_{9r} is the number we would expect to find if the respective plates gave a complete census of galaxies to magnitude 17.5 and no fainter. Applying these reductions to N_9 in the fourth column of the table, and dividing by nine, we get the number of galaxies per square degree ($\bar{N}_r$ in the last column), reduced to magnitude 17.5.

For example, when an A plate shows stars to magnitude 18.3, and 362 galaxies are counted in the central nine square degrees, we find

$$N_{9r} = 362 \times 10^{0.6(17.9 - 18.3)} = 208,$$

and $\bar{N}_r = 23.1$ is the computed average number of galaxies per square degree to magnitude 17.5 for that plate.

Because of the uneven population from plate to plate, and frequent unevenness in different parts of the same plate, the method is dependable only for the mean of many plates. It is the best we can do in the absence of magnitudes for the individual galaxies.[4]

2. See Sec. N of preceding chapter.
3. See the discussion in Chapter 7, Sec. G.
4. Of the several assistants who have worked on the survey of the north galactic polar zone, Ann B. Hearn has contributed most in bringing the in-

The total numbers of galaxies in the central nine square degrees of the 126 plates (without allowance for the small double counting on overlapping plates) are A plates, 34,119; MC plates, 21,507; total, 55,686.

In constructing Figure 26 we have indicated the essential completeness of the survey by taking the area of each plate equivalent to 25

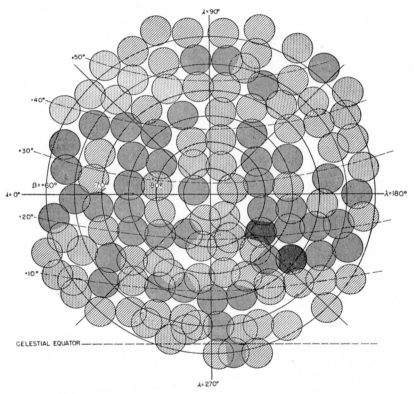

Figure 26. The distribution of galaxies to magnitude 17.5 in the north galactic polar zone, β +60° to β +90°. Shading indicates population per square degree; two darkest areas, more than 100 galaxies; next, 50 to 100; next (open diagonal lines), 30 to 50; and (dotted areas), under 30 per square degree. Another version of this diagram appears in Harv. Reprint 347 (1951).

square degrees. The plates actually cover nearly 35 square degrees, but the image quality for nebular discovery and measurement falls off

vestigations to a conclusion. The MC plates were all made by H. A. Sawyer, and the Bruce plates under the direction of J. S. Paraskevopoulos.

for the A plates outside the central nine square degrees, and for the MC plates outside the central 25 square degrees. The latter, however, require no magnitude correction within their central 25 square degrees.[5]

If we had used these larger MC areas rather than the central nine degrees, the tabulated values of $\bar{N}_r$ would not have been changed appreciably except for the plates:

Plate No.	25 Square Degrees	9 Square Degrees
MC 27134 where $\bar{N}_r$ would be 33.6 instead of 51.2		
31368	29.8	23.0
31440	62.0	24.6
32148	68.5	47.9
32872	34.1	92.2

The clustering of galaxies is the cause of these five large differences in the values of $\bar{N}_r$.

In the mean, for all MC plates, we have

$$\frac{\bar{N}_{r9} - \bar{N}_{r25}}{\bar{N}_{r9}} \div 69 = -4.2.$$

The outer sixteen square degrees therefore are on the average slightly richer than the nine square degrees in the plate center. From the smallness of the mean ratio we conclude again that a distance correction for counts on MC plates can be ignored in the census of galaxies. The total number of galaxies entering the survey of the north galactic polar zone can therefore appropriately be increased from the 55,686 of column 4, Appendix B, to 94,880. In addition, the outer unused parts of the A plates show approximately 35,000 galaxies, mostly brighter than magnitude 17.0, but for them there is considerable duplication through overlapping plates.

B. Comments on the census

Figure 26 illustrates again the irregularities in surface distribution that are now generally recognized as characteristic of the Inner Metagalaxy. When extensive areas are considered, the unevenness is largely smoothed out. Table 7 illustrates the similarity of $\bar{N}_r$ in the four quad-

5. *Proc. Nat. Acad. Sci., 26*, 554–61 (1940) (Harv. Reprint 208).

rants of galactic longitude, and the still closer similarity when the zone is divided into halves. The same small spread appears in the values of m_1 when the means are taken for intervals of galactic latitude. The greatest richness, shown by $\bar{N}_r$, is between latitudes $+70°$ and $+80°$, as Figure 26 also indicates. These surface inequalities might easily disappear as statistical fluctuations in the population if the census were taken a magnitude or two fainter.

Scattered over the zone are several clusters of galaxies, mostly with their individual members fainter than magnitude 17.5. No special attention is paid to them at this time because the Schmidt cameras can soon outline and analyze their content far better through adding two magnitudes to the depth of the survey.

Finally it should be noted that this north galactic polar zone is much richer per square degree to magnitude 17.5 than we have found in

Table 7. Regional Distribution

Region	Total N_{9r}	Plates	$\bar{N}_r$	$\bar{m}_1$
λ 0° to 90°	11,468	28	45.5	14.73
90 to 180	11,214	30	41.5	14.80
180 to 270	15,324	34	50.1	14.66
270 to 360	13,140	34	42.9	14.77
λ 0 to 180	22,682	58	43.5	14.76
180 to 360	28,464	68	46.5	14.71
90 to 270	26,538	64	46.1	14.72
270 to 90	24,608	62	44.1	14.75
β +57 to +70	27,855	75	41.3	14.80
70 to 80	18,103	37	54.4	14.60
80 to 90	5,188	14	41.2	14.80
All plates	51,146	126	45.1	14.74

the Harvard, Mount Wilson, and Lick surveys for the whole of the high-latitude sky, where the space-density parameter, m_1 falls between 15.1 and 15.2. Analysis of the last column of Appendix B shows that for the north galactic polar zone as a whole m_1 is 14.74; that is, it is four-tenths of a magnitude brighter than for the high-latitude sky average. This difference in m_1 corresponds to a factor of 1.75 in the average number of galaxies.

In Chapter 5 we found $m_1 = 15.16 \pm 0.02$ (m.e.) from a study of some 13,000 galaxies in the south galactic polar zone. This important inequality in registered population between north and south apparently cannot be attributed to differences in space absorption near the galactic plane (as was formerly thought) with the south having much heavier absorption. When galaxies to magnitude 19.0 are counted, the inequality between the north and the south largely disappears, and with it the hypothesis that local space absorption is responsible. We shall comment further on the contrasted distribution when density gradients are considered in Chapter 9.

C. Summary of the survey

(1) Working with long-exposure plates made with the Bruce and Metcalf doublets at the South African and Agassiz stations of the Harvard Observatory, we have investigated the distribution of approximately 95,000 galaxies brighter than magnitude 17.5 in the north galactic polar zone.

(2) About 95 per cent of the area with galactic latitudes greater than $+60°$ is covered by 126 plates, but since the counts could not be used dependably for the outer portion of the plates the galaxies have been tabulated for only 75 per cent of the area (Appendix B).

(3) The average population of galaxies over the whole zone is 45.1 per square degree to magnitude 17.5—a limit of brightness corresponding to a distance in the polar zones of about 150 million light years for galaxies of average luminosity. This northern population density appears to be about 1.75 times that of the south galactic polar zone. The distribution diagram illustrates the survey and indicates the degree of distributional irregularity.

(4) The important Virgo and Coma clusters of galaxies lie within the area surveyed, but the latter is too faint and the former too sparse to make significant contributions to the census.

CHAPTER 7. THREE LOWER-LATITUDE SURVEYS

A. Working in the celestial smog

We begin to suffer the consequences of the earth's location in a dust-affected region near the galactic plane when we extend the galaxy surveys from the polar zones toward the Milky Way. Even in the galactic latitude intervals between $+40°$ and $+20°$ and between $-40°$ and $-20°$ we cannot attribute the irregularities in the observed distribution of galaxies wholly to the inherently heterogeneous structure of the Metagalaxy; and from $±20°$ to the galactic equator the population varies from rich to poor to nothing, chiefly as a result of the blocking by the smog in our own spiral. When working in the galactic polar zones we have been observing through relatively small amounts of this interstellar dust and gas.

The three lower-latitude surveys reported in this chapter all exhibit the inherent unevenness, but more conspicuously they reveal through the deficiencies in metagalactic population the encroachments of the Milky Way dust clouds.

We may safely assume that about as many galaxies are concealed by the galactic dust as are in the clear.

Some 200,000 galaxies entered the examination of the north and south galactic polar zones reported in the two preceding chapters. An additional 150,000 have been recorded in other regions, in low and intermediate latitudes. Three of these regions are now examined for evidence of the effect of the Milky Way on the census of the Metagalaxy. They were described briefly under Regions A, B, and F in Chapter 2.

B. The south celestial polar zone

In supplementing the brief report in Chapter 2, we now turn to some details of the census of the south celestial polar zone (decl. $-60°$ to $-90°$) to show, among other things, the large difference in galaxy

frequency in the important environs of the two Magellanic Clouds.[1]
The work on the individual magnitudes of 36,000 galaxies in this
zone permits us to examine the distribution in apparent brightness
(magnitude-frequency curves) and note the occasional large population irregularities in depth. For various reasons the magnitudes are
only approximate, but they still are useful in this preliminary survey.
The mean error is less than two-tenths of a magnitude; but fainter
than the 17th magnitude the sequences, which have been based mainly
on star counts, are yet provisional, and the systematic errors may approximate half a magnitude. The long-exposure plates actually cover
completely only 88 per cent of the polar zone. For the brighter objects,
however, additional plates have been used and the coverage is complete.

In the Harvard *Tercentenary Papers* of the Observatory,[2] the individual photographic magnitudes and approximate positions in galactic
coordinates are given for all 36,000 objects. These magnitudes will
provide a useful source of photometric data on galaxies when the
adopted sequences of magnitudes have been improved by further work
on photometric standards.

In Appendix C we summarize the results and give for each plate
the galactic coordinates, the number of galaxies marked and measured
in the total area of 35 square degrees, the average number per square
degree brighter than magnitude 17.5 in the central nine square degrees, and $m_{n(s)}$, the apparent magnitude of the limit of completeness
for galaxy discovery, except for the plates centered in low latitude
where the number of galaxies is too few for the derivation of the nebular magnitude limit. For such plates the stellar magnitude limit is given
in parentheses.[3] The number of objects falsely identified as external
galaxies (perhaps 3 per cent) is believed to be practically balanced by
the number of objects that have been overlooked or wrongly dis-
carded. The false inclusions and exclusions are more common toward
the plate edges, as well as near the photographic limit of the plates and

1. I am indebted to Mrs. Muriel M. Seyfert for assistance in the examination
of the plates and in the determination of the magnitudes, all of which were
twice measured.

2. *Harv. Ann., 105*, No. 8 (1937)

3. From Table 1 of *Harv. Ann. 105*, 140f. (1937). See also *Proc. Nat. Acad.
Sci., 23*, 449 (1937) (Harv. Reprint 140).

near the borders of the Milky Way. Less than 1 per cent of the galaxies in this survey have been previously observed.

The values of m_n in the last column of Appendix C are derived from the frequency plots of the nebular magnitudes, and on the average are 0.34 magnitude brighter than m_s, the stellar magnitude limits, which are actually about 0.2 magnitude above the faintest stellar image.

The south celestial zone is not rich in bright galaxies. In the 2,760 square degrees there are only 343 objects brighter than the 15th magnitude. Figure 27 shows their distribution. There are only a few in the difficult low latitudes, and some of those plotted are now found on re-examination on better plates not to be external galaxies. Of the

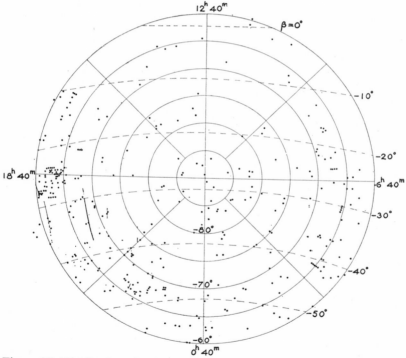

Figure 27. Distribution of galaxies brighter than magnitude 15.0 in the south celestial polar zone. Full circles and radial lines designate declination and right ascension, respectively, and the broken lines are arcs of galactic latitude.

twelve objects within ten degrees of the galactic circle only the following appear certainly extragalactic:

| | Galactic Coordinates | | | |
Object	β	λ	Magnitude	Type
NGC 3136	—9°	255°	12.4	E1
Anon. 1	—9	256	14.5	E4
Anon. 22	—4	279	14:	E2
Anon. 3	—10	282	14.8	E1

The first two are the brightest members of a small group of low-latitude galaxies in the semitransparent region in Carina. It includes the S-shaped spiral IC 2554, magnitude 15.0. The Eta Carinae nebulosity is only 7° away. The region merits close investigation for faint variable stars in the interest of evaluating galactic extent in that direction. The other eight objects brighter than magnitude 15 with $\beta \leqslant 10°$ are probably gaseous or planetary nebulae or star groups.

Many of the brighter objects of this zone are included in the Dreyer *New General Catalogue* (*NGC*), but not all. Only 103 of the 343 objects brighter than the 15th magnitude are in that listing, and only 71 additional objects are in the *Index Catalogues* (*IC*). Of those fainter than the 15th magnitude among the 36,000 here recorded, there are 234 *IC* objects and 68 in the *NGC*. The existing general catalogues contain but one-half of the galaxies between magnitudes 13 and 15, and relatively few that are fainter. In our surveys of the Inner Metagalaxy only about 1 per cent of the galaxies are brighter than the 15th magnitude. These tiresome figures are presented only to indicate that the *NGC* and *IC* are indeed poor indicators of the galaxy population.

The cluster of bright galaxies at the left edge of Figure 27 (18^h 40^m, —60° to —65°) is the only conspicuous group with members brighter than the 17th magnitude in the whole area. It lies in latitude —25°, not far from a galactic "window" that is described in Chapter 11. To the limit of the present survey there are in the polar zone only a few other groups of galaxies. One of them falls on a rich plate only 6° from the south celestial pole. So far as shown by the available photographs it is composed of approximately 200 members, scattered somewhat irregularly over an area of 1.5 square degrees. Its galactic coordinates are 276°, —31°. On the asumption of 0.3 magnitude of space absorption, its distance is more than 300 million light years.

In Figure 28, which shows the distribution in lots of 35 square degrees of all the galaxies in this polar zone brighter than magnitude 17.5, the region of the cluster of bright objects shown in Figure 27 is not outstanding. Again we caution that among the faint objects recorded for latitudes lower than ±10° there are many that may be planetaries, star groups, or diffuse nebulosities. The crowding of the galactic stars has made the survey in these lowest-latitude fields not dependable.

C. Background of the Magellanic Clouds

The most striking feature of the distribution of faint galaxies in the south celestial polar zone is the contrast in population between the

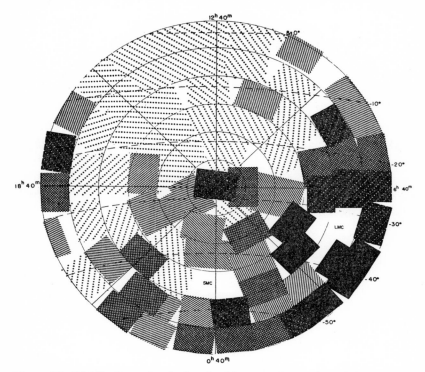

Figure 28. Distribution of galaxies, in 35-square-degree lots, brighter than magnitude 17.5. Coordinates as for Figure 27. Shading increases with population density. SMC and LMC designate areas of the Small and Large Magellanic Clouds. The other open areas are not covered by long-exposure Bruce plates.

neighborhoods of the Small and Large Magellanic Clouds. No attempt was made in this first census to study the few galaxies within the boundaries of the Magellanic Clouds where it is difficult to distinguish between the nebulosities and clusters that are actually in the Clouds and the external systems seen through them. From the scarcity of recognizable galaxies within their boundaries we have assumed that there is considerable local absorption, at least in their central regions.

The metagalactic richness in the vicinity of the Large Cloud and the relatvely low number of galaxies around the Small Cloud are shown in Figure 28. On the north and west borders of the Large Cloud (the galactic latitude of its center is —33°) the population brighter than magnitude 17.5 is shown numerically by the survey of 36 square degrees on four plates in the accompanying table. The nebu-

Plate	Quality	Latitude	m_n	$\bar{N}_{17.5}$
A 17163	5	—38°	17.6	48.3
16350	4	—40	17.3	41.9
17187	5	—39	17.6	59.0
16732	4	—37	17.5	60.0
Means	4.5	—38.5	17.5	52.5

lar magnitude limit of completeness is given in the fourth column, and in the last column there is given for each plate the mean number of galaxies per square degree brighter than magnitude 17.5.[4]

On the east side of the Large Cloud three plates (mean latitude —26°) show that brighter than magnitude 17.5 the population is only one-third as dense per square degree (second table).

Plate	Quality	Latitude	m_n	$\bar{N}_{17.5}$
A 16368	6	—28°	17.5	15.2
16758	4	—26	18.0	18.6
14256	8	—25	17.4	18.1
Means	6	—26.3	17.63	17.3

The seven plates of good quality (mean latitude —44°) surrounding the Small Cloud (latitude of center —45°) show a subnormal population of about 9.0 galaxies per square degree to the same magnitude limit—a value that is but 43 per cent of the average for the whole of the high-latitude sky. It is less than 20 per cent of that 15° away on

---

4. This tabulation and the two following are derived from material given in *Harv. Ann., 105*, No. 8 (1937).

the north and west borders of the Large Cloud. The third table gives the data for the environs of the Small Cloud.

Plate	Quality	Latitude	m_n	$\bar{N}_{17.5}$
A 17198	7	—40°	18.1	6.1
17222	5	—50	18.5	18.6
17144	5	—48	17.9	5.8
17150	5	—45	17.6	12.3
14395	4	—41	18.0	7.8
16299	7	—44	18.5	4.4
17194	6	—40	17.7	8.1
Means	5.6	—44	18.04	9.0

D. Metagalactic excesses and deficiencies

If space absorption between us and the area of the Small Cloud were wholly responsible for the deficiency in comparison with the whole high-latitude sky, the light loss would need to be 0.6 magnitude. It would need to be 1.2 magnitudes to bring the population up to that recorded on the north and west sides of the Large Cloud. That absorption around the Small Cloud of this large amount is not responsible for the deficiency down to magnitude 17.5 is suggested by the more or less normal frequency in the affected region which is attained at magnitude 18.0 on some of the plates that record fainter magnitudes. For example, near the south pole, plate A 16945 (decl. —85°, lat. —30°), which records only 9.2 galaxies per square degree brighter than 17.5, is well above average population at 18.0.[5] Actual scarcity rather than space absorption may thus be the cause of much of the low recorded population at and around the pole. A census of 20th magnitude galaxies would settle the matter.[6]

5. The cluster of galaxies mentioned on page 96 contributes a part of the excess. See Harv. Ann., 105, 141, n. 11 (1937).

6. Before leaving this subject of uneven distribution, we should note that the mean value of m_n in the vicinity of the Small Cloud is half a magnitude fainter than around the Large Cloud, although the plates, as shown by the plate numbers, were made in the same season. This difference in magnitude limit could be attributed to an error in the magnitude systems used for the photometry near one Cloud or the other. Suppose we grant that error and put the m_n for the Small Cloud at 17.5 also. Then the reduction of the number of galaxies to 17.5 need not be made and $\bar{N}$ would be about 18.0 for the Small Cloud, which is still but a third of the value for the Large Cloud. Such a correction would still leave untouched the evidence of the metagalactic cloud of galaxies in the vicinity of the Large Magellanic Cloud, but the deficiency

Unpublished material from Bruce photographs, not yet fully analyzed, shows the extension of the rich metagalactic aggregation or "stream" of galaxies, extending from the Large Cloud for 20° or more in the general direction of the south galactic pole. (There is a reference to this stream in Chapter 5.) A special study [7] of the magnitudes and the distribution of galaxies over 122.5 square degrees in the Horologium part of this extended stream shows, with $\bar{N}_{17.5} = 49$, about double the average for the high-latitude sky.

In summary, the evidence is good that in our census we have come upon a great elongated metagalactic cloud of galaxies in the southern hemisphere, a decided excess over the average. Of equal interest, a metagalactic deficiency appears in the region of the south celestial pole, extending out as far from the Milky Way as the Small Magellanic Cloud. Only a part of this deficiency, and that chiefly within 15° of the galactic circle, are we inclined to attribute to light absorption. The eventual extension of the survey to the 20th magnitude will test the present evidence.

E. Magnitude frequencies

The diagrams in Figure 29 show for four typical plates the degree of uniformity (and nonuniformity) in the distribution of galaxies over four areas, each of nine square degrees. This figure illustrates *surface* distribution. It does not indicate the actual magnitudes of objects represented by the points. We know, however, that the magnitudes are almost entirely in the interval between 15 and 18. The *depth* distribution is indicated by the magnitude frequencies for four typical plates in Figure 30. The observed deviations from smoothly rising density curves (such as the plotted $log\ N = 0.6m +$ const.), in the interval from magnitude 15 to the magnitude of maximum frequency, include not only the irregularities in the density of population but also whatever difference there may be from place to place in the spread of

---

around the Small Cloud would not be as conspicuous as before, when it was one-fifth. If, on the other hand, the error were assumed to be in the magnitude system for plates in the neighborhood of the Large Magellanic Cloud, for which the nebular magnitude limits do seem to be less faint than average for the Bruce plates, and if the error were in the right direction to ameliorate the discrepancy, the discrepancy would still be one-third, and the deficiency in galaxy population around the Small Cloud would be very conspicuous as before.

7. *Harv. Ann., 88,* No. 5 (1935).

absolute luminosities among the galaxies. In the absence of clear evidence to the contrary, we assume the same spread wherever a considerable sampling is made. It is probable, therefore, that some of the maxima in the frequency curves, as for c and d in Figure 30, indicate the presence of localized groups and not merely peculiarities in the frequency of intrinsic luminosities.

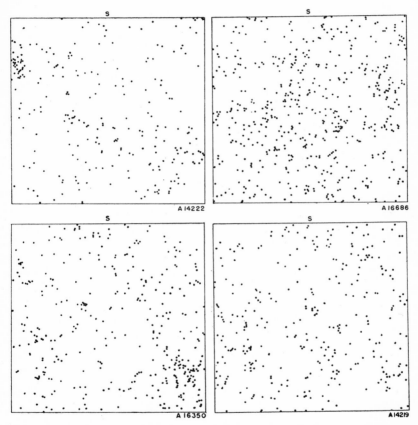

Figure 29. Irregularities in surface distribution of galaxies on four typical plates: A 14222 at 18^h 54^m, −62°7; A 16686 at 4^h 40^m, −75°; A 16350 at 4^h 20^m, −62°5; A 14219 at 22^h 33^m, −67°6

F. An edge or center of the Metagalaxy?

The magnitudes of the 36,000 galaxies in this polar zone provide an opportunity to examine the evidence, in the direction of the south celestial pole, for a general falling off of population with distance (as though we were approaching the "edge of the universe"), or an increase of population with distance (as though we were approaching a "center" in the Metagalaxy). The irregularities with distance (brightness) for only four individual plates are shown in Figure 30.

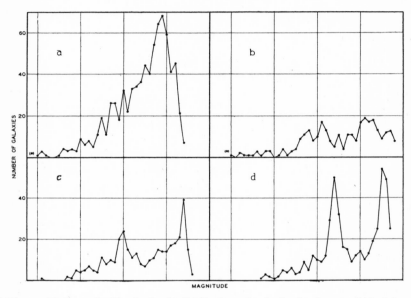

Figure 30. Irregularities in depth distribution of galaxies for four typical plates

Taking the material for 42 plates with galactic latitudes higher than 25° (not including the six overrich plates north and west of the Large Cloud), we can smooth out local irregularities and uncover whatever the general tendency may be, as shown in Figure 31, where the logarithm of the number of galaxies in 10th-of-a-magnitude intervals is plotted against the apparent magnitudes. The straight line in the figure indicates the expected frequency on the hypothesis of uniform space density. If the six rich regions around the Large Magellanic Cloud were included with the 42 other plates, a pronounced deviation from the straight-line relation would become obvious at photographic magnitude 16.5, which probably marks the brightness and implies the distance at which the metagalactic cloud referred to above becomes effective in our census of galaxies in the south celestial polar zone.

The close agreement of the observations with the straight line representing average uniformity (Fig. 31) indicates that for the distance out to at least 150 million light years (for galaxies of average luminosity) there is in the direction of the south celestial pole neither rise

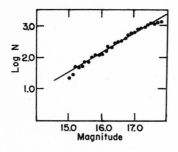

Figure 31.
Relation of the logarithm
of the number of galaxies
to apparent magnitude
for 42 plates with galactic
latitude higher than 25°

nor fall of population density. Brighter than magnitude 15, the number of galaxies is too small to give a useful point in the diagram, and beyond 17.5 for most of the plates the data are incomplete. If we use only the galaxy magnitudes from the plates that provide satisfactory magnitudes to 18.5, corresponding to a distance for average galaxies of about 250 million light years, we again find no thinning out or increasing of the population with distance. As indicated in Chapter 5 for the south galactic polar zone, there is not as yet a metagalactic center or border in sight.

G. Galaxies of the Polaris region

The most dependable photographic magnitudes of a large number of faint galaxies are probably those derived for some 16,600 objects in an area of 1,240 square degrees around the north celestial pole.[8] The higher than average accuracy is due to the availability in this region of the North Polar Standards of stellar magnitude and to the suitability of the Metcalf camera at the Agassiz Station for work on both nebular and stellar images between magnitudes 15 and 18. The photographic glass plates made with this 16-inch camera (MC series) are bent during exposure by air pressure in order to fit them closely to the focal

8. Harlow Shapley and Rebecca Jones, *Harv. Ann., 106,* 1–38 (1938). Possibly the magnitudes of the 22,000 galaxies in the decl. + 43° belt are as good, or even better because of better sky position. See Sec. E of the next chapter.

surface of the lens combination. As a result of this adjustment there is very little effect of distance from the optical axis on the shapes and densities of the photographic images. An investigation of the flatness of field is reported in *Harvard Annals, 106*, 6f. (1938).

The relatively small number of galaxies in this northern region has been noted by Hubble and others; and at Harvard attention has been called to the clouds of obscuring matter in the vicinity of the North Pole and the consequent reddening of standard sequence stars through space absorption.

A summary of the observational material is given in Appendix D for the 52 long-exposure plates that have been examined and measured in detail. In addition, plates made with smaller cameras have been used for the magnitudes of objects brighter than 15.5, and some additional plates of the MC series, overlapping those of Appendix D, cover most of the small gaps between plates. In this area only 263 nebular objects had heretofore been published, most of which are in the *New General Catalogue* of Dreyer.

The general character of our work on galaxies in the north celestial polar zone is very similar to that described above for the southern celestial polar region. The summary in Appendix D is in practically the same form as that for the southern survey (Appendix C), except that $\bar{N}$ now gives for 25 square degrees, instead of nine, the average number of galaxies per square degree brighter than magnitude 17.6 (instead of 17.5). The plates that do not record completely the galaxies to that magnitude, or that go fainter, have been reduced to 17.6 by means of the usual formula for bringing galaxy survey plates to a common magnitude limit. The numbers in parentheses in the last column again give the stellar magnitude limit m_s for those plates where in low latitude the number of galaxies is too few for the derivation of a reliable nebular magnitude limit m_n.

Figure 32 shows the distribution of the quantities m_s for the 52 plates and of $m_s - m_n$ for the 38 plates on which the number of galaxies is sufficient to permit, from the plot of the frequency of galaxy magnitudes, a fair estimate of m_n. In the mean, the difference $m_s - m_n$ is just less than half a magnitude. The magnitude of each individual galaxy has been twice estimated, and when the two estimates differed by more than three-tenths of a magnitude we made a third independent estimate. The individual magnitudes, the stellar magnitude limit, and rough positions for the individual plates are published in *Harvard Annals, 106,* No. 1 (1936).

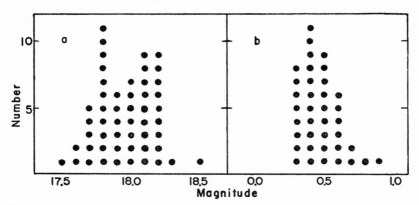

Figure 32. Distribution of (a) m_s and (b) $m_s - m_n$ in the north celestial polar zone

H. The galaxies around the North Pole

The distribution over the polar zone of all the measured galaxies brighter than magnitude 17.6 is shown in Figure 33, where the coordinates grid shows right ascension, declination, and galactic latitude. The plotted points do not give the exact positions of individual objects; but the number found in each square degree is represented in the plot by that number of points evenly distributed over the square degree (with appropriate adjustment for overlapping plates). The diagram shows: 1) the almost complete absence of galaxies in the lower galactic latitudes; 2) a somewhat patchy distribution over the whole area within 20° of the North Pole; 3) a few heavy concentrations of galaxies, indicative of the presence of physical groups. But there were only two distinct clusters of galaxies recognized in our survey of the polar zone. One is centered at 17^h 15^m, $+72°5$. It covers 1.1 square degrees, and with a correction for the general field is found to contain 85 cluster members to the limit of the plate, $m_s = 18.2$. The other cluster is centered at 17^h 12^m, $+78°3$, with an area of 1.5 square degrees and a cluster population of about 100 galaxies to magnitude 17.8. These clusters will be more fully outlined and many others revealed in the north polar zone when the surveys are taken to the 19th magnitude and fainter by larger instruments.

Either because of general and abnormally heavy space absorption, or more probably because of a structural detail of the Metagalaxy, the population is low over the whole zone in comparison with the regions in similar latitudes but other longitudes. It does not seem likely that the deficiency can be attributed to the failure of the nebular magnitude system (brighter than 17.5), or to the telescopes, since elsewhere the MC plates have revealed the normal population of galaxies. The magnitude sequences are independently determined on each plate and satisfactorily checked with the sequences in the neighboring Selected Areas and with the North Polar Standards.

I. North Polar Sequence in obscuring dust

As shown in an earlier chapter, the average value of $\bar{N}_{17.5}$ for the whole high-latitude sky is 24 (for galaxies brighter than 17.6). For

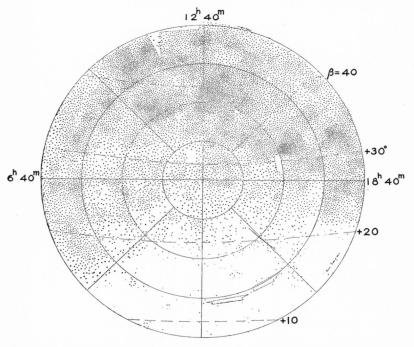

Figure 33. Distribution of galaxies brighter than magnitude 17.6 within 20° of the north celestial pole, with broken lines indicating galactic latitudes. Noteworthy is the fact that Polaris and the basic North Polar Magnitude Sequence are in a region affected by considerable space absorption.

the 52 plates of this census the value is one-third as much, $\bar{N}_{17.5} =$ 8.8. For the 29 plates centered in latitudes higher than $+25°$ it is 12.9, and for the twenty plates in latitudes higher than $+30°$ it is still only 14.1. The chart in Figure 33 shows rather definitely the extension of the "flare of darkness" up from the Milky Way to the North Pole and beyond. But the foregoing values seem to indicate a strong absorption in addition to a patchy obscuration. If we take only the nine plates in latitudes greater than $+29°$ that appear, on the basis of nebular distribution, to be free of space absorption, we find that the average number of galaxies per square degree (brighter than magnitude 17.6) is 16.2. The ratio of this number to that for the average high-latitude sky gives for the general absorption $\Delta m = 1.67$ log $(24/16.2) = 0.3$, but the assumption of a subaverage population, like that around the Small Magellanic Cloud, would provide an equally good explanation of the observed deficiency.

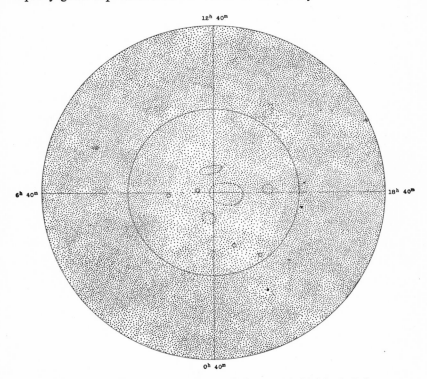

Figure 34. Distribution of stars within 10° of the North Pole

For the four fields centered within 5° of the North Pole, we have $\bar{N}_{17.5} = 1.4$ and for the 15 fields within 10° of the North Pole, $\bar{N} = 7.5$. The North Polar Standard Sequence, therefore, is located in a region affected patchily by half a magnitude of absorption ($\Delta m = 1.67 \log (14.1/7.5) = 0.46$), relative to the fields in this polar zone with latitudes higher than $+30°$. The colors of these standards must of course also be affected (made redder) by the absorbing material, which presumably lies at least in part between us and the faint stars of the North Polar Sequence.

If the Milky Way absorption that extends over the Pole lies between us and the stars of apparent magnitude 13.5, its effect should be revealed in the star counts that are represented by Figure 34, where the distribution of stars within 10° of the North Pole is plotted from counts made on a Harvard patrol plate (scale: 1 mm = 10′). The 21,000 stars brighter than magnitude 13.6 show an unevenness of distribution that is almost certainly due to absorption. In this plot the regions containing the stars of the North Polar Sequence are indicated by the dotted closed curves. The star count should be carried a few magnitudes fainter to test more fully the effects of intervening space absorption.

Area	Right Ascension	Declination	Approximate Area (square degrees)
1	5^h 55^m	+77°	7
2	7 40	+77	10
3	10 50	+86.5	5
4	11 30	+77	6
5	13 0	+74	6
6	19 0	+76	4

On the galaxy distribution chart (Fig. 33) six of the more conspicuous low-density regions, in galactic latitudes greater than $+25°$, have the positions and areas shown in the table. The central 2 square degrees of No. 3 are heavily obscured [9] by a dark cloud that appears to be some 2,000 light years distant.

9. See also Lois T. Slocum and B. W. Sitterly, *Harv. Bul.*, No. 905, 18 (1937).

J. The Canopy

In Chapter 2 the survey of the so-called Canopy, which involves about 78,000 individual galaxies in 3,600 square degrees, was briefly described. It covers an important part of the northern sky that is rich in bright galaxies and somewhat above the average population for faint galaxies to the 18th magnitude. The region includes the whole of the constellations Draco and Ursa Minor, most of Lynx and Ursa Major, and considerable portions of Canes Venatici, Boötes, Hercules, and Camelopardalis. The census is based on 153 long-exposure plates made chiefly by H. A. Sawyer with the Metcalf camera at the Agassiz Station.

Since the main object of this survey of northern galaxies was to examine the true clustering and intrinsic distributional irregularities (as distinguished from the uneven blocking in low latitudes by interstellar obscuring clouds), no fields nearer the Milky Way than galactic latitude $+20°$ are included. This limitation has also the advantage of minimizing the misidentifications that frequently occur in the richer star fields of low latitude. We believe that the survey is reasonably complete, and that here again the erroneous inclusions (estimated at about 3 per cent of the entries) are balanced, on the average, by the overlooked galaxies which are generally of the spheroidal type. The degree of accuracy of the identifications has been sample-checked with the aid of the large reflectors.

Only the surface distribution (not the depth distribution) is considered in the discussion of the Canopy.[10] The counts of galaxies have all been reduced to a common magnitude limit $\bar{m}_n = 17.5$. All galaxies within 100 million light years, with absolute magnitudes brighter than -15, are thus included, but the dwarfs at that distance are of course too faint for the survey.

K. Tables and diagrams of the Canopy galaxies

In Appendix E the observational material is summarized with plate centers given only in galactic coordinates. The magnitude limit m_s

10. *Proc. Nat. Acad. Sci., 36,* 157–66 (1950). Rebecca B. Jones and Virginia McKibben Nail have assisted in the plate examination and the numerical discussion, respectively.

refers to stars, and $\bar{N}_r$ is the number of galaxies per square degree averaged over the 25 square degrees that are usable on each plate. These numbers have been reduced to magnitude 17.90, which is the mean of the stellar magnitude limits for the 153 plates. The actual number of galaxies marked and counted on the central 25 square degrees of each plate can be computed if desired from

$$N_{25} = 25\bar{N}_r \times 10^{-0.6(17.9-m_s)}.$$

The data for each square degree of each plate have been published in *Harvard Annals, 88,* No. 7 (1950).

The distribution of the galaxies in the Canopy is shown graphically in galactic coordinates (with two declination arcs superposed) in Figures 35 and 36, the former indicating the density of population plate by plate, and the latter showing the population by the approximate plotting of the individual galaxies. In Figure 35 each circular area is centered on a plate center and covers 20 square degrees. There is some overlapping, especially at the north celestial pole, marked by a small circle at $\lambda\,90°$, $\beta\,+28°$. The actual coverage is more complete than this diagram indicates, since each plate actually covers 35 square degrees. There are, in fact, scarcely any gaps between plates.

L. Distribution of Canopy galaxies in latitude and longitude

Two results derived in earlier analyses, both of significance in the cosmography of external galaxies, are confirmed by the Canopy study. The first is a demonstration of the far extension of the "Cepheus flare" or cloud of absorbing material that comes out of the Milky Way between galactic longitudes 70° and 110°. It is shown here to extend up to galactic latitude $+37°$, in longitude 105°. This flare of absorption covers the north celestial pole and, as pointed out earlier in this chapter, indicates that the North Polar magnitude standards are involved. The Canopy census includes much of the north celestial polar zone.

The second result supported by this survey is the evidence that from galactic latitude $+40°$ to the north *galactic* pole there is no appreciable net increase of population density with latitude. Whatever apparent increase there might be as a result of absorption near the galactic plane is lost in the inherent irregularities of distribution. This result was first reported in the Darwin Lecture in 1934 [11] and later verified in an exploration of the declination 5° belt ($+41$ to $+46°$) by Shapley and Jones—a study that is reported in the next chapter. The relation of population to latitude, as shown in the Canopy survey, is summarized in Table 8. The mean numbers per square degree have

Table 8. Mean Number of Galaxies per Square Degree

(Number of fields in parenthesis)

Galactic Latitude	Longitude Intervals				
	30°–59°	60°–89°	90°–119°	120°–149°	30°–149°
20°–29°	12.1 (9)	9.2 (12)	7.2 (11)	11.1 (10)	9.7 (42)
30°–39	18.8 (9)	22.6 (10)	11.6 (10)	21.1 (7)	18.3 (36)
40°–49	28.0 (6)	26.0 (9)	20.7 (9)	24.5 (7)	24.5 (31)
50°–59	26.6 (5)	31.0 (7)	31.8 (7)	28.6 (7)	29.7 (26)
>60	19.4 (4)	34.6 (5)	33.5 (6)	22.3 (3)	28.8 (18)
>40	25.2 (15)	29.7 (21)	27.7 (22)	25.8 (17)	27.4 (75)
All	19.9 (33)	22.3 (43)	18.7 (43)	20.5 (34)	20.4 (153)

been reduced for this tabulation to the common apparent magnitude 17.9. The greatest density of population when all longitudes are considered (last column) is in the neighborhood of galactic latitude $+60°$.

M. Irregularity in distribution

The clustering of galaxies is now generally recognized, and the population chart in Figure 36 is consistent with results found elsewhere in the sky. Except for the region of the Cepheus flare, obscuration by interstellar dust clouds appears to be ineffective for the high-latitude sections of the Canopy. If we examine the population inequalities from plate to plate for five intervals of galactic latitude we get the following display of the deviations:

Latitude interval	20°–30°	30°–40°	40°–50°	50°–59°	> 59°
Number of plates	42	36	31	22	22
Average deviation	±0.65	±0.99	±1.16	±1.87	±1.84

The average deviation from the mean population for each group increases with latitude, as a result, presumably, of the decreasing number of plates. The irregularities in the real distribution, as might be expected, appear to be independent of galactic latitude.

11. *Mon. Not. Roy. Ast. Soc., 94,* 812 (1934).

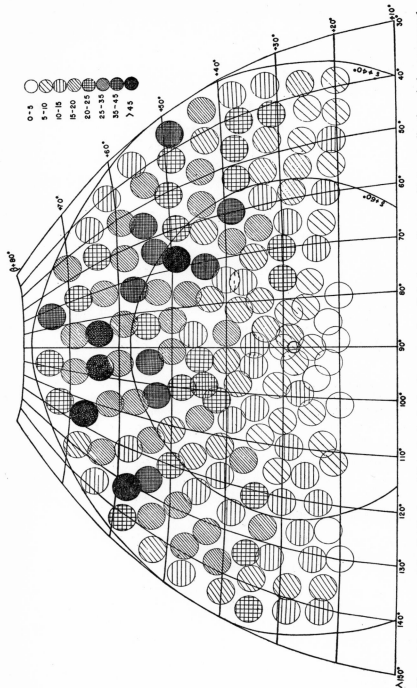

Figure 35. Summary of the distribution of the galaxies in the Canopy region. Galactic coordinates, with two declination circles superposed.

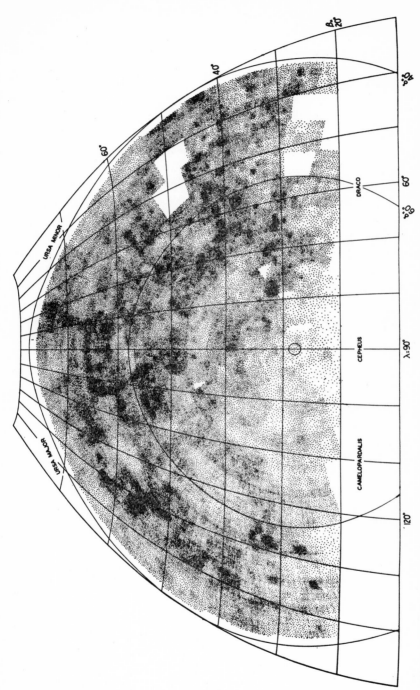

Figure 36. Plot of 78,000 individual galaxies in the Canopy area. Coordinates as for Figure 35. A few plates are yet to be examined.

The Canopy survey shows, of course, a number of rich clusters or clouds of galaxies. Deeper search to magnitude 20 and fainter will certainly reveal scores of new clusters and clarify others that are here only suggested.

N. A billion galaxies within reach

Through the Bowl of the Big Dipper, which lies in the Canopy, we have recorded in our metagalactic census 1,500 galaxies. Twelve of them are brighter than magnitude 12.8, with *NGC* 3998, at magnitude 11.5, the most conspicuous. If, as we believe, the radial densities are approximately constant throughout the volume we are surveying—i.e., the population density does not decrease or increase with distance— the number of galaxies quadruples with every fainter magnitude. Accordingly, the Hale telescope on Mount Palomar, with long exposures on fast plates, could photograph more than a million galaxies through the Bowl of the Dipper. This striking picture emphasizes the impressively large population of the Metagalaxy. The Dipper's Bowl covers less than a thousandth of the sky. With proper allowance for space absorption in low latitudes, we compute that a billion galaxies are within reach of our present telescopic power. This number, of course, assumes that there is no serious thinning-out up to distances of the order of two billion light years, and such an assumption may be precarious. But essentially uniform density out to a distance of one billion light years is a reasonable deduction from the evidence now on hand.

In the next chapter we shall further examine the latitude effect— that is, the variation of galaxy population with the angular distance from the galactic circle.

CHAPTER 8. GALACTIC LATITUDE AND METAGALACTIC POPULATION

A. North rich; south poor

A century ago the investigators of nebulous sidereal objects noticed the relatively greater abundance of galaxies in the northern galactic hemisphere. The conspicuous spirals and spheroidals in Virgo and in the neighboring constellations to the north had been noted by the Herschels who, of course, did not identify them as external systems. R. A. Proctor and other writers of the late 19th century commented on the absence of spirals and other "white nebulae" from low latitudes. When the important role of interstellar dust in the blotting out of the light of galaxies was recognized, it was natural to assume that the relative poorness in bright galaxies in the southern galactic hemisphere might be the result of a greater amount of light absorption on that side of the observer.

The various indications that the sun is possibly a hundred light years north of the plane supported the assumption that light absorption concentrated narrowly along the galactic plane might be largely responsible for the unequal distribution of bright galaxies. This ad hoc hypothesis was not really disposed of until the Harvard and Mount Wilson surveys of galaxies fainter than the 16th magnitude were analyzed. In a special examination of the asymmetry in population we found the ratios given in the table.[1] Definitely for the brighter gal-

North/south = 1.9 for galaxies with magnitudes brighter than 12
    = 1.6 " " " " between 12 and 13
    = 1.4 " " " " " 14 and 18
    = 1.3 " " " " " 16 and 18
    = 1.0 " " " " " 19 and 20

axies the north is rich, the south poor. To the extent that we can depend on the magnitudes fainter than the 16th, we can adopt the approach to equality when we go fainter as implying that absorption

1. *Harv. Bul.,* No. 894, 5–13 (1934).

near the galactic circle is not the cause of the conspicuously unequal populations of bright galaxies at the 12th magnitude. To explain the inequality we must again appeal to real differences on the two sides of the galactic plane. Apparently there is a population gradient across the Milky Way, which is additional evidence of the nonhomogeneity in metagalactic structure that will be considered in a later chapter.

The dust clouds along the Milky Way plane, although not responsible for the asymmetry in the apparent distribution of bright galaxies in high latitudes, are properly held responsible, however, for the "latitude" effect in the census of galaxies in and near the Milky Way. Formerly this effect was inversely called "the tendency of the white nebulae to concentrate at the galactic poles"—a concept that pre-dated the general acceptance of the fact that the spirals are extra-galactic stellar systems.

A question that is now little asked— Is the absorbing layer of dust so smooth and symmetrical that the absorption may be accurately estimated by a formula that relates absorption to galactic latitude alone?—has been answered in the negative by the studies of nebular distribution. The dust layers along the galactic plane are not uniform or smooth, except in a very rough first approximation.

An early investigation of the latitude effect was made by Hubble. His sampling of the population characteristics at all latitudes and in a wide range of longitude led him to the construction of the well known diagram that is here reproduced as Figure 37. The unevenness of the population, especially in low latitudes, found by him and earlier surveyors, should have fully confirmed the suspicion that a formula depending on latitude alone would fail from place to place; but nevertheless Hubble and many followers have in practice used his formula,[2]

$$\log N = 2.115 - 0.15 \csc \beta,$$

where β is the galactic latitude and N is the number of galaxies.

From the colors of stars and galaxies, as well as from evidence provided by the Harvard galaxy survey, we have found a surprisingly high transparency of space in the galactic polar zones. There appears to be practically no general space absorption in much of the high-latitude area. The total absence of absorption in latitude $-20°$ in

2. Edwin P. Hubble, *Astroph. Jour.*, *79*, 49 (1934).

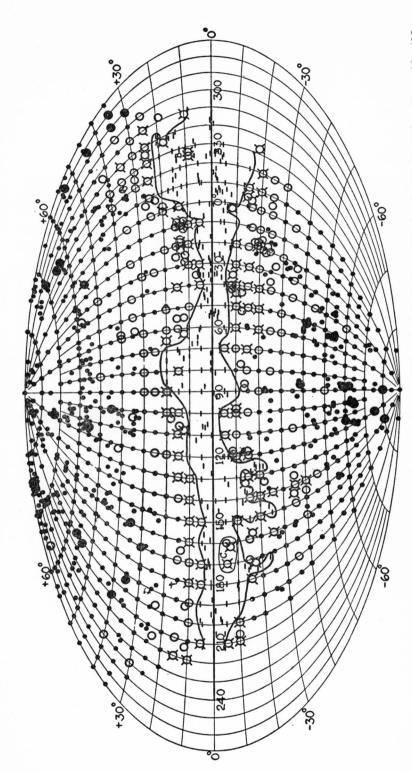

Figure 37. Hubble's chart of the distribution of galaxies in 765 "reflector fields" north of declination −30°, described in *Mt. Wilson Contr.*, No. 485 (1934)

the direction of the Andromeda Nebula has recently been reported.[3] Nevertheless, while awaiting further determinations, we shall use $\Delta m = 0.25$ for the absorption of photographic light in all latitudes higher than $\pm 50°$.

B. The width of the absorption zone

Two special surveys with the Bruce and Metcalf telescopes of the Harvard Observatory bear on the width of the zone of strong absorption near the Milky Way and on the progression of transparency with increasing latitude. These surveys are based on considerably larger areas and numbers than were used by Hubble, but even so they fail to provide a general formula that would indicate the nature of the absorption near the galactic plane. Apparently too much irregularity prevails in the space distribution of dust clouds and of galaxies to permit formulization.

C. The width as shown by the Bruce camera for southern galaxies

Our first study at the Harvard Observatory of the latitude effect is sufficiently illustrated by one tabulation and two diagrams.[4] For the test, we photographed with the 24-inch Bruce camera at the Boyden Station nearly 30,000 galaxies on 358 long-exposure plates, with centers in all latitudes from $+90°$ to $-90°$. Table 9 summarizes the material. The counts were used for only the central nine square degrees of each plate. Obvious clusters of galaxies, five in number, were omitted in deriving average populations for intervals of galactic latitude. The faintest limits of stellar magnitude were determined for each plate by the usual star-count method.

In the fourth column of Table 9 the means of the logarithms of the numbers of galaxies per square degree are given for each interval of latitude without correction for the varying plate limits, and in the fifth column the average deviation from the mean logarithms. In the sixth and seventh columns are the means of the logarithms and the average deviations after appropriate correction of the number of galaxies on each plate to the number that would be found if the stellar magnitude

3. A. D. Code and T. E. Houck, 1956 meeting of the American Astronomical Society at Columbus; abstract in *Ast. Jour., 61* (1956).

4. *Proc. Nat. Acad. Sci., 19,* 389–93 (1933) (Harv. Reprint 90).

limit were 18.2. (We assume, for reduction purposes only, that the distribution in depth is uniform for each separate region.)

The values in the fourth and sixth columns of Table 9 are plotted against galactic latitude for Figure 38, with the crosses indicating the corrected values. The plates that were made during the rainy seasons at the Bloemfontein station do not on the average go as faint as those made in the dry seasons, with the result, as shown in the figure, that in the northern galactic hemisphere the reduction to magnitude 18.2 consistently increases the number of galaxies.

Table 9. Distribution of Galaxies in Galactic Latitude

Galactic Latitude Intervals	Square Degrees	Mean Galactic Latitude	Mean Log N	Average Deviation	Mean Log N_r	Average Deviation
−90 to −81	54	−83.0	1.26	±0.10	0.97	±0.16
−80 to −71	90	−76.2	1.37	0.24	1.17	0.37
−70 to −61	108	−64.3	1.29	0.30	1.09	0.26
−60 to −51	234	−54.3	1.09	0.32	1.20	0.41
−50 to −41	369	−45.8	1.05	0.29	1.05	0.36
−40 to −36	135	−37.4	0.78	0.42	0.82	0.42
−35 to −31	189	−32.9	0.87	0.46	1.08	0.57
−30 to −26	180	−28.2	0.62	0.54	0.71	0.52
−25 to −21	252	−23.2	+0.46	0.42	0.56	0.55
−20 to −16	216	−17.7	−0.04	0.55	. . .	. . .
−15 to −11	180	−13.1	−0.42	0.49	. . .	. . .
−10 to 0	108	− 6.5	−0.28	0.41	. . .	. . .
0 to +10	144	+ 6.7	−0.64	0.35	. . .	. . .
+11 to +15	99	+13.7	−0.21	0.43	. . .	. . .
+16 to +20	90	+18.6	+0.16	0.47	. . .	. . .
+21 to +25	54	+22.8	0.81	0.36	1.02	0.18
+26 to +30	54	+27.6	1.23	0.28	1.48	0.33
+31 to +35	117	+33.0	1.02	0.36	1.30	0.37
+36 to +40	99	+37.2	1.19	0.26	1.36	0.23
+41 to +50	162	+45.0	1.28	0.24	1.42	0.25
+51 to +60	90	+54.7	1.20	0.17	1.44	0.24
+61 to +70	99	+65.4	1.21	0.20	1.45	0.14
+71 to +80	72	+74.6	1.27	0.21	1.32	0.23
+81 to +90	27	+85.2	1.30	0.42	1.44	0.73

Near the Milky Way, from latitude −20° to +20°, it has not been possible to derive dependable stellar magnitude limits for use in the reduction to a standard value; there are accordingly gaps for this interval of latitude in the last two columns of Table 9 and in Figure 38.

The distribution of the 358 fields in galactic coordinates is shown in Figure 39, where the dots refer to fields in northern latitudes. The large dots and circles indicate the richer fields. This diagram again illustrates the unevenness in galaxy distribution over the sky and the absence of recorded galaxies in the regions near the Milky Way, β 0° to ±10°.

Returning to Figure 38, we can point out three significant features. The first is the variation of the mean values of log N with galactic latitude—a result bearing on the old problem of the "concentration of galaxies to the galactic poles." There is in the mean no certain change with latitude north of +25°. South of —25°, however, toward the south galactic pole, the mean density increases, but some recognized streamers of dark nebulosity in latitudes —20° to —40° are partially responsible for the low population in these latitudes. If this early survey had included the later counts for the rich regions in Horologium between latitudes —40° and —60°, much of the slope here recorded on the population curve for latitudes from —40° to the South Pole would have been eliminated.

The second point of interest is the large size of the tabulated mean deviations, in both the original galaxy counts and the numbers after

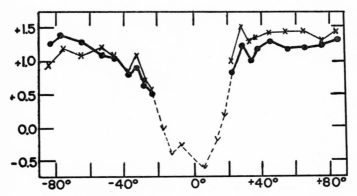

Figure 38. Distribution of galaxies in galactic latitude. Ordinates are logarithms of the average number per square degree, and abscissae, galactic latitudes. Values derived directly from counts are indicated by dots; crosses represent values reduced to magnitude limit 18.2. Between β —20° and β +20° the mean points are indefinite because of the total absence of galaxies from some regions.

reduction to the magnitude limit 18.2 for stars. These deviations indicate numerically the conspicuous nonuniformity in the distribution of galaxies throughout this large region of 3,222 square degrees. The irregularities are, in fact, so great from field to field that it is probably meaningless to speak either of a progression of average density with galactic latitude or of its absence.

The third feature that is worth noting is the greater richness of the northern galactic hemisphere. For latitudes between —40° and —90° the average number of galaxies per square degree to the stellar limit 18.2 is 12.6; between +40° and +90° it is 26.1. (This last value is erroneously given as 17.8 in Harvard Reprint 90 (1933).)

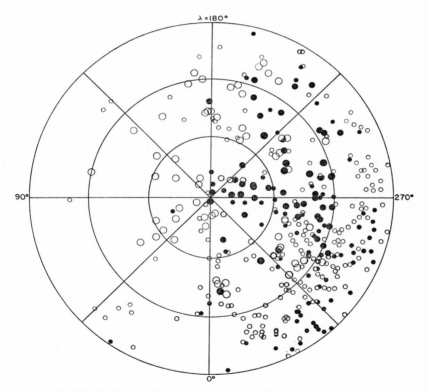

Figure 39. Distribution of fields in galactic coordinates. Filled circles indicate northern latitudes, open circles southern latitudes. The larger circles show galaxy population greater than 15 galaxies per square degree and small circles population less than 16 galaxies per square degree.

D. *Early Lick Observatory measures of latitude effect*

Although he himself did not feel that the galaxy counts, derived from small-field plates made with the Crossley Reflector at the Lick Observatory, were sufficient for a reliable test of the population variation with latitude, Mayall, in a figure which is reproduced herewith (Fig. 40), provides a definite confirmation of the first of the results described above.[5] North of latitude +40° he finds no increase in average population with latitude. The data for southern latitudes is but half as extensive, but it essentially confirms the results from the Harvard survey. There is also confirmation of the flatness of the population curve north of galactic latitude +40° in Hubble's results, especially for his "survey" fields.[6]

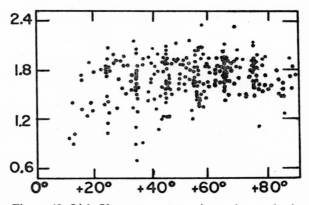

Figure 40. Lick Observatory survey in northern galactic hemisphere. Coordinates are latitudes and logarithms of numbers of galaxies. From *Lick Observatory Bul., 16,* 196 (1934)

The coescant formula clearly is not applicable to the distribution of galaxies in the northern galactic hemisphere.

E. *Width as shown by the Metcalf triplet for the northern hemisphere*

The investigation with the Bruce telescope was based largely on counts in southern fields. Of the 358 plates less than a tenth were centered

5. Nicholas U. Mayall, *Lick Bul., 16,* 196 (1934).
6. *Astroph. Jour., 79,* Table XI (1934).

north of the celestial equator. A second examination [7] of the problem has been undertaken in the course of a photometric survey of 22,000 galaxies in a northern declination belt—a zone 5° wide extending around the sky, bounded by declinations +41° and +46°. This particular declination belt was chosen because it is zenithal at the Agassiz Station of the Harvard Observatory, and the magnitude standards of the twelve Kapteyn Selected Areas at declination +45° are conveniently located on the plates. Therefore homogeneous series of nebular magnitudes could be derived, as well as data on the relation of latitude to galaxy population.

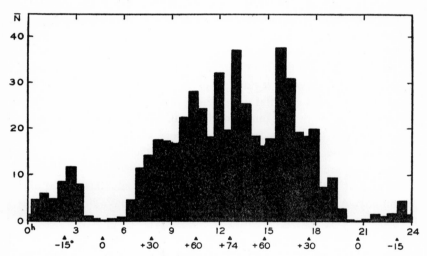

Figure 41. Distribution of galaxies to magnitude 17.5 along the five-degree zone. Abscissae are both hours of right ascension and degrees of galactic latitude; ordinates are numbers of galaxies per square degree.

The photometric results are given in Harvard Reprint 208 to an extent sufficient for a general analysis. The magnitudes of the 22,000 galaxies are probably the most homogeneous and accurate yet obtained by photographic methods for a large number of galaxies,[8]

7. Harlow Shapley and Rebecca B. Jones, *Proc. Nat. Acad. Sci., 26,* 554–61, 599–604 (1940) (Harv. Reprints 208 and 209).

8. Again Henry A. Sawyer was the photographer with the 16-inch Metcalf camera at the Agassiz Station during the five years in which we were accumulating the material, and Rebecca B. Jones was the principal measurer of the photographic magnitudes.

although the work in the Polaris region is comparable, and is in second place only because of the greater zenith distances necessary for the plates of the north polar zone.

For our present examination of the latitude effect it will suffice to show the results graphically in Figure 41. The conclusions from these data are so similar to those derived in our preceding study of southern fields that little further comment is necessary. This declination 5° belt does not get nearer to the north galactic pole than latitude +75°, and in the southern galactic hemisphere the belt gets no further than 20° from the Milky Way circle. The survey is therefore essentially an examination of the latitude effect, in the northern galactic hemisphere only, for two widely separated intervals of longitude.

The evidence presented here and elsewhere in this volume of the essential clarity of the high-latitude sky must not be taken to prove the complete absence of either general absorption or scattered streaks of nebulosity. In several regions in intermediate latitudes such as at the north and south celestial poles, there is clear evidence of flares of obscuration extending far out from the Milky Way. Even in the galactic polar zones there may be faint dark and bright nebulosities that could affect the galaxy census slightly. To detect such obstructions, further work must be done with high-speed, short-focus photographic cameras and with the increasingly sensitive instrumentation of radio astronomy. Already from the radio telescopes we have indications in the polar zones of thin clouds of neutral hydrogen. Also faint optical traces of nebulosity in highest latitudes have been reported tentatively on photographs made with the Palomar 48-inch Schmidt telescope.

CHAPTER 9. GALAXY GROUPS AND COSMIC GRADIENTS

A. Clusters of galaxies *

In the literature of extragalactic systems we find many discussions of a few individual clusters of galaxies—studies of groups that appear definitely to be physical organizations, presumably maintained, even if only weakly, by the mutual gravitational attraction of their members. One of the most seriously studied aggregations is the Wolf cluster in Coma; another is the relatively nearby [1] large cloud in Virgo (Fig. 42), which provides good material for research on metagalactic dynamics.

Several other groups similar to the fairly compact system in Coma are involved in Humason's radial velocity measures which are basic to the concept of the expanding universe, for example, the clusters in Corona Borealis, Boötes, and Ursa Major. But some of these systems lie beyond the bounds selected for the present treatise on the Inner Metagalaxy. In Fornax, however, is a sparse but useful group of bright galaxies, notable for a few supergiant spheroidal systems, and in Centaurus a very rich elongated aggregation that should perhaps be called a cloud of galaxies rather than a cluster. Since the membership is numbered in thousands,[2] it should be a happy hunting ground for large southern telescopes. Another group, discovered by Wolf [3] in Perseus, is important because of its low latitude and the presence of radio sources which apparently are located in the group as a whole and in a pair of galaxies that may be "in collission." (See Chapter 11, § D.)

The photometry of 25 fairly compact clusters of galaxies which have appeared in various sections of our metagalactic surveys has

---

* For a discussion and a bibliography of the work on double galaxies see Thornton Page, *Astroph. Jour., 116,* 63–80 (1952), and Erik Holmberg, *Lund Ann., 6* (1937) and *Astroph. Jour., 92,* 200–34 (1940).

1. Approximately 20 million light years distant.
2. *Harv. Bul.,* No. 874, 9–12 (1930).
3. Max Wolf, *Ast. Nach., 170,* 211 (1906).

been published in summarized form.[4] But it was clear from the first examination of long-exposure Bruce plates that literally hundreds, perhaps thousands, of such physical groups could be sorted out of the general field of galaxies if the limits of the census were pushed one or two magnitudes fainter and if "cluster" were broadly defined. This abundance of groups is indicated, for example, by the clumpiness revealed in the plots of faint galaxies in the Canopy region of the northern sky, described in Chapter 7, and in the distribution charts prepared by Shane and his colleagues at the Lick Observatory.[5]

The Mount Wilson–Palomar annual report for 1954–55, summarized in *Astronomical Journal, 60,* 296 (1955), indicates the nature of Zwicky's intensive program on the statistics of clusters of galaxies: "The distribution of about one thousand clusters of galaxies was investigated in thirty fields taken with the 48-inch Schmidt telescope, each covering forty square degrees. Large spherically symmetrical clusters of galaxies were found to have consistent characteristics independent of distance. No evidence was found for a clustering of clusters to form super-clusters."

It seems scarcely profitable to discuss the clustering problems here on the basis of the present limited data, since studies of the groups and clouds can soon be carried to greater depths by the Lick, Palomar, and forthcoming southern metagalactic surveys. It should suffice in this chapter to recognize the urgency and importance of future studies of galactic clustering and to describe briefly some of the clusters and clouds so far investigated.

B. The Virgo Cloud

In Chapter 3, Figures 9 and 10 outline the size and form of the important aggregation that stretches more than 15 million light years from Coma through Virgo to the edge of Centaurus. Several papers on the magnitudes, types, and dimensions of the galaxies in the central Virgo clustering (around decl. $+12°$) have been published from the Harvard Observatory.[6] At Mount Wilson the motions in the line of

4. *Proc. Nat. Acad. Sci., 19,* 591–6, 1,001–6 (1933) (Harv. Reprints 92 and 102).

5. C. D. Shane and C. A. Wirtanen, *Proc. Am. Phil. Soc., 94,* 13–17 (1950); *Ast. Jour., 59,* 285–304 (1954).

6. For example, Harlow Shapley and Adelaide Ames, *Harv. Bul.,* No. 865, 1–13 (1929).

sight have been studied by Humason and Hubble,[7] and photoelectric magnitudes by Pettit [8] and by Stebbins and Whitford.[9] Treating the group as a dynamical system, Smith [10] deduced such high masses for the galaxies that attention has turned to the possibility of much intergalactic material in that region of the sky, or a heavy population of low-luminosity stars in the individual galaxies. With the largest reflectors, stars and star clusters can be identified in many of the brighter galaxies of the group. The study of these systems, and of the similarly distant bright galaxies in the Canopy to the north, will therefore assist greatly in establishing a dependable correlation of distances with brightness.

C. Wolf's "Nebelneste"

Among the studies of this important group of faint galaxies near the north galactic pole are the following:

1. An early Heidelberg catalogue of the positions, and descriptions on the Herschel system, of 1,528 nebulae in and around the cluster.[11]

2. Hubble and Humason's [12] survey of the distribution of objects in the central part of the cluster where about 800 with photographic magnitudes between 14 and 19.5 are loosely concentrated.

3. Photometry by Shapley of 1,766 galaxies brighter than 18.5 in and around the cluster,[13] and a comparison with the Mount Wilson census (Fig. 43). About 500 of the galaxies are within the cluster proper and a large proportion of the other 1,300 are members of the metagalactic cloud of which the Coma cluster appears to be a nucleus. See ¶ 8 below.

4. Lundmark's [14] measures on Mount Wilson plates of the diameters of 280 of the objects in Wolf's catalogue.

5. The Spitzer-Baade [15] hypothesis that the members are now

7. *Astroph. Jour.*, *74*, 43–80 (1931) (*Mt. Wilson Contr.*, No. 427), and by Humason, *Astroph. Jour.*, *83*, 10–22 (1936) (*Mt. Wilson Contr.*, No. 531).
8. *Astroph. Jour.*, *120*, 413–38 (1954).
9. *Ibid.*, *115*, 284–91 (1952).
10. *Astroph. Jour.*, *83*, 23–30 (1936) (*Mt. Wilson Contr.*, No. 532).
11. Max Wolf, *Heid. Publ.*, *1*, 125 (1902)
12. *Astroph. Jour.*, *74*, 43–80 (1931) (*Mt. Wilson Contr.*, No. 427).
13. *Harv. Bul.*, No. 896 (1934).
14. *Uppsala Medd.*, No. 30 (1927).
15. *Astroph. Jour.*, *113*, 413–18 (1951).

chiefly of Classes S_0 and E because of galaxy collisions (interpenetrations); the interstellar dust, from which spiral-arm stars evolve, has been swept out of the individual galaxies.

6. Omer's [16] study of the distribution of galaxies and the total mass of the cluster.

7. Hubble and Humason's [17] measures of the radial velocities of several of the galaxies and the derivation of a recession of about 7,000 kilometers a second.

8. Zwicky's [18] study of the structure of the cluster, as shown on the Palomar Schmidt plates, in which he reports the diameter is not 1° but something like 10°.

9. David S. Heeschen's detection with the Agassiz Station's 24-foot radio telescope of neutral hydrogen radiation (21 cm) from the cluster as a whole, and his evidence that the enveloping hydrogen cloud has a mass 10^{14} times that of the sun's and receeds at about 7,000 km/sec. (*Astroph. Jour., 124*, 660 [1956].)

D. Wolf's Perseus cluster

This group of galaxies lies in a Harvard low-latitude variable star field (VSF 199). Because of its transparency the field is useful in the determination of the extent of the Milky Way in the anti-center direction (see Chapter 11). The cluster contains more than 100 galaxies, the brightest of which is of magnitude 12.7.

E. Photometry of 25 clusters of galaxies

Until the revision was made in 1953 of the distance scale for external galaxies, our own Galaxy appeared to be definitely outsized—the largest of all—an uncomfortable and unlikely situation. The possibility of finding larger galaxies than ours was one of the reasons for the writer's photometric survey of 25 remote clusters, many of which are parts of metagalactic clouds.[19] From these physically associated groups we can readily sort out and measure the giant galaxies. The search for a supergiant was not very successful. The estimated average diameter for the 2,650 galaxies measured in the 25 clusters is about the same

16. *Ast. Jour., 55*, 178–9 (1950); *57*, 22 (1952).
17. *Astroph. Jour., 74*, 43–80 (1931) (*Mt. Wilson Contr.*, No. 427).
18. *Pub. Ast. Soc. Pac., 63*, 61–71 (1951).
19. See note 4.

as the diameter of the Small Magellanic Cloud. Incidentally, this result may be the most important finding of the research. The brightest 125 galaxies in the 25 groups did not exceed in any clear case the dimensions of the Andromeda Nebula (M 31).

The revision of the distance scale has, however, quite altered the comparison with our Galaxy. Linear diameters of distant galaxies are now considered to be about three times the values formerly estimated. Several of the leading members of these remote clusters are therefore probably more extensive and certainly more luminous than our galactic system. The discomfort of being outstanding in the Metagalaxy is therefore considerably ameliorated.

F. Two large metagalactic clusters

In the later investigations of two large southern clusters of galaxies, Miss Boyd and the writer [20] examined 1) the general luminosity curve of galaxies (frequency distribution of absolute magnitudes), and 2) the mean density of matter in "unexpanded" regions of metagalactic space. The general luminosity curves, based on nearly 8,000 galaxies and shown in apparent magnitudes in Figure 44, can be referred to the absolute magnitude system when a final evaluation of the distance scale for faint galaxies has been determined. A tentative estimate of the distance (revised) is 90 megaparsecs for group A, 115 megaparsecs for group B. The corresponding distance moduli, $m - M = 34.8$ and $m - M = 35.3$, show that in these groups are many giant galaxies comparable with our own. They are our equal in brightness if not in measurable dimensions.

A by-product of this investigation is an estimate of the mean density of matter throughout a cluster of galaxies that presumably is not itself in expansion, although the group as a whole participates in the metagalactic recessions. The mean density of group B, which is illustrated in Figure 45, is found to be something greater than 10^{-28} g/cc, which is about one hundred times the mean density in general metagalactic space. This ratio will be unaffected by alterations in the distance scale.

20. *Proc. Nat. Acad. Sci., 26,* 41–9 (1940) (Harv. Reprint 185).

G. *The local family*

The most interesting metagalactic group is not one that we can see or photograph as a cluster. It is composed of the surrounding neighbors. We construct a cluster out of our measures of the distances of nearby galaxies, bright and faint. The dominant bodies are of course our Galaxy, the Andromeda Nebula, and Messier 33 (Fig. 46). Cosmically more significant than these three conspicuous spirals are the dwarf galaxies that in recent years have come to light as members of our neighborhood. Three of these obscure dwarfs have been known, to be sure, for about a century: *NGC* 187, *NGC* 285, *IC* 1613. *NGC* 6822 was discovered in 1885. Close examination with large reflectors, however, was necessary to show certainly that these four are neighbors, as are also the intermediate Magellanic Clouds and the dwarf companions of the Andromeda Nebula, *NGC* 205 and Messier 32. Of the uncatalogued dwarf neighbors, two were found on the Harvard plates—the Sculptor and Fornax superclusters; the others in the course of the Mount Wilson–Palomar surveys. We are in doubt about the distance of some of these neighboring galaxies but apparently all are within a radius of 600 kiloparsecs, which is about ten times the distance to the nearest external galaxies, the Magellanic Clouds.

As mentioned in Chapter 3, the spirals apparently are not the most frequent type when the whole population of a given volume of space is explored. The most common galaxies are the dwarf open spheroids of the Sculptor type and the irregular systems like *IC* 1613 (Table 10). In the writer's view, many of these dwarf galaxies may not really be units of the local family but members rather of the general field in which the dwarfs can be known only when nearby.[21]

Among the more distant galaxies we see many examples of half a dozen clustering together. Our local group may be of that sort. Authentic members of the physical group, on this hypothesis, would be the Magellanic Clouds, Messier 33, our Galaxy, and the Andromeda Nebula trio—all with negative latitudes indicating that our galactic system is on the edge of the group. There may be, of course, two or three members concealed behind the low-latitude smog. Hubble has

---

21. *Pub. Univ. Mich., 10,* 81 (1951).

suspected three spirals [22]—*NGC* 6946, *IC* 342, and *IC* 10—and at Harvard we find another possible member, *NGC* 2427, on the edge of the southern Milky Way.[23] The distances of these suspected objects cannot be closely estimated because of the heavy intervening obscuration: eventually measurements of color excesses may settle the question of membership.

Table 10. Members of the Local Group of Galaxies

Name	R.A. (1900)		Decl.	Longitude	Latitude	Type
Our Galaxy	...	...	...	...	...	Sb
NGC 147	0^h	30^{m}4	48°2	87°	—14°	Ep
185	0	36.1	48.1	89	—14	Ep
205	0	37.6	41.4	89	—21	E5p
M 31	0	40.0	41.0	89	—20	Sb
32	0	40.0	40.6	89	—22	E2
SMC	0	50	—73	269	—45	Irr
Sculptor	0	57.5	—34.0	241	—83	Ep
IC 1613	1	00.6	1.7	99	—60	Irr
M 33	1	31.1	30.4	103	—31	Sc
Fornax	2	37.5	—34.7	203	—64	Ep
LMC	5	26	—69	247	—33	Irr-SB
Leo I	10	05.8	12.6	194	+50	Ep
Leo II	11	10.8	22.4	189	+69	Ep
Ursa Minor	15	08.2	67.3	71	+45	Ep
Draco	17	19.4	58.0	53	+34	Ep
NGC 6822	19	42.1	—14.9	354	—20	Irr

H. Neighboring dwarf field galaxies

A quantitative indication of the population of the local family can be offered. In Chapter 5 we found that in metagalactic space galaxies of all sizes are separated on the average by a million light years, except in the clusters and dense clouds. If with our Galaxy as the center we take two million light years as the radius of the observed domain of the local family, we should have about 35 galaxies within that distance. We have already found nearly twenty of them. Others will undoubtedly be added to the list. In other words, from the galaxy counts in the south galactic polar zone, we derive a space-density parameter

22. Edwin P. Hubble, *The Realm of the Nebulae* (New Haven, 1936), pp. 145 ff.

23. Harlow Shapley and Ann B. Hearn, *Ast. Jour.*, *59*, 169 (1954).

which suggests that the local family is largely an illusion; it is probably little more than a group of six or eight conspicuous objects in a continuous field of dwarfish spheroidal and irregular galaxies of typically low luminosity (absolute magnitude below —14.5). Such groups, as mentioned above, are not uncommon; the best known is Stephan's quintet in Pegasus (Fig. 47) and Seyfert's sextet in Serpens.[24]

I. Density gradients

The data published for the thousand brightest galaxies in the Shapley-Ames catalogue show conspicuous unevenness in surface and space distribution. Attention was called in Chapter 3 to a local density gradient, more or less perpendicular to the galactic plane, which produces on the north side, compared with the south, a much greater richness in the galaxy population between the 10th and 16th magnitudes.

Notwithstanding the approximate uniformity in population density when very large volumes of space are averaged, there is evidence of measurable density gradients in other parts of the sky, and in at least two large areas there appear to be pronounced transverse density gradients that should be of considerable significance in the reconstruction of the early history of the Metagalaxy. In particular, the Bruce survey of the southern sky has revealed among the galaxies, at distances of some 200 million light years, a major unevenness in surface distribution that apparently cannot be written off as due to localized clusterings of galaxies or to systematic errors in our magnitude standards. The number of 18th magnitude galaxies per square degree doubles in going from the vicinity of the south galactic pole some 40° in the direction of the Large Magellanic Cloud. But when the future surveys reach to the 19th magnitude, these apparent inequalities may diminish. It is unlikely, though not impossible, that high-latitude space absorption contributes seriously to the observed deficiency in population density in the south galactic polar zone. The distribution of high-latitude faint stars shows no corresponding effect, and intergalactic absorption, lying beyond the bounds of our galactic system, is not likely to be involved.[25] Much more probably we have here a large

24. *Pub. Ast. Soc. Pac.*, *63*, 72 (1951).
25. See Chapter 14 for a specific examination of this question of the high-latitude frequency of 18th magnitude stars and galaxies, and Harvard Reprints

Figure 42. A section of the Virgo Cloud of bright galaxies

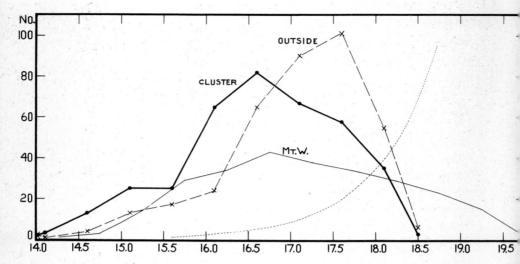

Figure 43. Luminosity curves for the Coma cluster. Heavy line, Harvard survey after correction f[..] superposed field, which is indicated by the dotted line. Light line, Mount Wilson survey of cent[..] of cluster, corrected for field. Broken line with crosses, Harvard survey of region of 30 squa[..] degrees around cluster. Abscissae are photographic magnitudes; ordinates are galaxy numbers in ha[..] magnitude intervals.

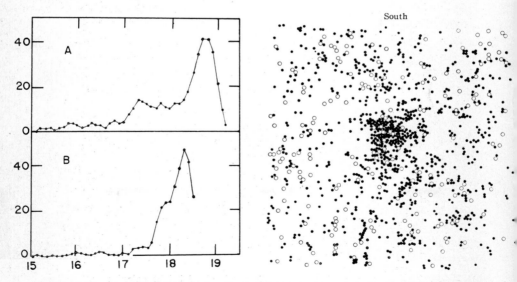

Figure 44 (*left*). Luminosity curves for Group A (above) and Group B. Ordinates are numbers [..] galaxies; abscissae, apparent photographic magnitudes. Figure 45 (*right*). Distribution of galaxi[..] in four square degrees centered on Group B. Objects fainter than magnitude 17.5 are indicated [..] dots, brighter objects by open circles. Stars in this field are not plotted.

Figure 46. Messier 33, one of the nearest spiral galaxies. Mt. Wilson photograph

Figure 47. Stephan's Quintet—another "local family"

structural inequality in the outer part of what we call the Inner Metagalaxy.

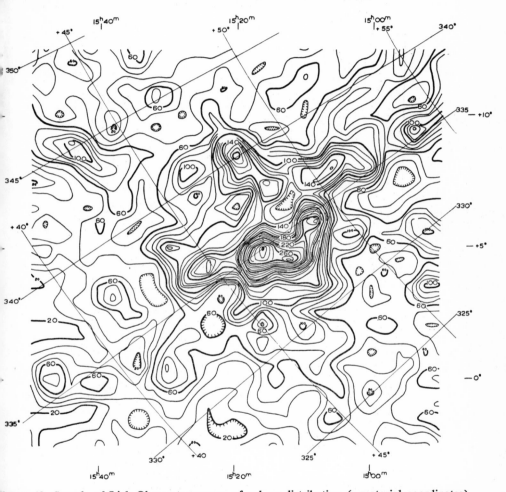

Figure 48. Sample of Lick Observatory maps of galaxy distribution (equatorial coordinates).
st. Jour. 59, 303 (1954)

Although the writer has examined some of the transverse gradients
with the aid of hundreds of long-exposure photographs showing more

150 and 154 for the data and diagrams bearing on the rich clouds of galaxies
that suggest the transverse density gradient. This particular part of the sky
is perhaps where we should look in search for the hypothetical "center" or
"nucleus" of the expanding Metagalaxy.

than 100,000 galaxies, it does not seem worth while to elaborate on the results in this place, since comprehensive deeper probes will soon become available. Better tests can be made of transverse gradients,

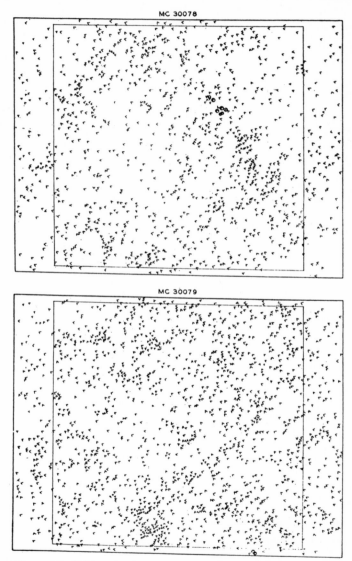

Figure 49. Galaxy distribution on two plates with centers at λ 36°, β +49°. (MC 30079) and at λ 144°, β + 52° (MC 30078)

and eventually of radial gradients, when the Lick survey is completed. Figure 48 shows a contour map constructed from galaxy counts by Shane. Metagalactic structure is suggested, and some of the concentrated clusters of distant galaxies begin to emerge; but what would the population of this same area look like if we took the magnitude surveys to the 22d magnitude?

The general problem of "clumpiness" and of clusters of clusters is under study by Neyman and Scott,[26] and recently by David Layzer.[27] Illustrations of clumpiness and of deficiencies, which could be repeated a hundred times by plates in the Harvard, Lick, and Palomar collections, appear in Figure 49, where the distribution is shown of galaxies in two fields of high latitude, far from troubles with uneven space absorption.

26. *Astroph. Jour., 116,* 144–63 (1952).
27. *Ast. Jour., 61,* 383 (1956) (Harv. Reprint II, 89).

CHAPTER 10. THE SOUTHERN MILKY WAY—ITS DUST AND GAS [1]

A. The southern sky

The greater richness of the southern celestial hemisphere when compared with the northern is illustrated by its brightest constellations, Scorpius, Sagittarius, Centaurus, and Crux, and by such stellar giants in brightness and size as Sirius, Antares, Canopus, and Achernar. It is the hemisphere of the nearest external galaxies (the Magellanic Clouds) and of the central nucleus of our Milky Way. More than four-fifths of the known globular star clusters, including the two brightest, Omega Centauri and 47 Tucanae, are also southern, as is the heavily obscured Messier 4, probably the nearest of all globular clusters.[2] But the outstanding feature of the southern sky is the Milky Way, distinguished by the brilliance of the gaseous nebulosities in Orion, Carina, and Sagittarius, and by the darkness of the large obscurations among the Milky Way star clouds, in particular the darkness of the Coalsack in Crux and the complex of obscurities around Rho Ophiuchi.

An examination of the opacity of the discrete nebulosities and of the general interstellar dust that obscures the distant parts of the southern Milky Way is reported in this chapter. The study is a significant part of our account of the Inner Metagalaxy since it concerns the nature of our own system and makes practical use of thousands of remote galaxies.

B. Zones of Obscuration

On the basis of galaxy counts on photographs made with the Mount Wilson reflectors, E. P. Hubble published in 1934 his well known

1. This chapter on the opacity of the southern Milky Way, in essentially its present form, was printed in the *Proceedings of the National Academy of Science*, November 1955. It is Harvard Reprint 427, the twenty-third paper in the series Galactic and Extragalactic Studies. Jacqueline Sweeney was co-author.
2. Jesse L. Greenstein, *Astroph. Jour., 90,* 387 (1939).

picture of the distribution of faint galaxies (Chapter 8, Fig. 37). He was able to take his sampling survey southward only to declination —30°. Hubble's work on northern galaxies is in the way of being reinforced, or actually supplanted, by the full-coverage atlas of the northern sky by C. D. Shane and his co-workers at the Lick Observatory and by the Schmidt camera Atlas prepared on Mount Palomar with the collaboration of the National Geographic Society. The Lick survey extends in the southern sky as far as declination —23°, and the Palomar Sky Atlas to declination —27°. Further south the only general coverage is that provided by the Bruce telescope at the Boyden Station of the Harvard Observatory, with some support provided in recent years by the Armagh-Dunsink-Harvard (ADH) Baker-Schmidt reflector at that station.

The principal value of Hubble's survey was its outlining of the Region or Zone of "Avoidance." The term, incidentally, is a misnomer. It was first used by the writer in pointing out the apparent absence of globular clusters in galactic latitudes lower than ±5°, and later adopted by Hubble in describing the similar but wider "avoidance" of the Milky Way by the galaxies. Properly speaking, in both cases we are dealing with a Region of Obscuration. Behind the dust clouds of the Milky Way there is undoubtedly a more or less uniform population of external galaxies, and probably in the direction of the galactic center there are many undiscovered low-latitude globular star clusters.

C. The Harvard census of southern galaxies

The plates available from the Boyden Station of the Harvard Observatory make possible a thorough check on the Region of Obscuration, both for the northern sky, where, however, the work can best be furthered through the Lick and Palomar surveys, and for the southern sky, where the Bruce plates provide complete coverage. The investigation here reported deals with the galaxy population, and the derivation of the dust cloud opacity, for a region that covers one-fifth of the whole sky. The survey extends in galactic longitude from 200° to 340°, in galactic latitude from +30° to —30°. More than 400 long-exposure photographs have been used and approximately 60,000 galaxies marked. The plates record stars fainter than the 18th magnitude and galaxies to magnitudes between 17.5 and 18.0, the limits depending on the speed of the photographic emulsions and the sky conditions. In this survey we adopt 17.7 as the average photographic magnitude limit for galaxies.

In latitudes lower than ±20° we cannot satisfactorily use the star-count method to set up magnitude sequences or to determine on each plate the faintest magnitudes for stars or galaxies. We have, therefore, in this survey assumed all plates to be equally penetrating when proper corrections are made for exposure time and plate quality. In this respect our method follows that used by Hubble in his sampling surveys. For 9 per cent of the 415 plates, exposures deviate appreciably from the standard three hours, and corrections have been made to the galaxy counts as follows:

Exposure Time	Number of Plates	Correction Factor
100^m to 120^m	2	1.50
120 to 150	10	1.25
> 210	26	0.80

The results of the survey are best shown in the diagrams of Figures 50 and 52, described below. They extend, in a sense, Hubble's northern sampling survey to the remainder of the Milky Way, but with a much fuller coverage. The tabular presentation of the data used for the diagrams is published in the *Harvard Annals, 106,* No. 3 (1955).

In addition to the 415 Bruce plates represented in the tabulation and the diagrams, a large number of additional long-exposure Bruce photographs, and some plates made with other telescopes, have been used for checking. The earliest of the plates were made in 1898, but only 18 prior to 1910, and therefore the work depends chiefly on modern emulsions—Cramer Hi-Speed and Eastman 103a-O. Most of the photographic work was done under the supervision of John S. Paraskevopoulos, late superintendent of the Boyden Station. The examination of the plates has been carried out by a number of assistants, all of whom have had extensive experience in the detection of galaxy images; but the principal workers in the examination of the plates and the construction of the diagrams have been Jacqueline Sweeney, Pedro Kokaras, Ann B. Hearn, and Catherine M. Hanley. The writer examined and qualified all plates and also examined nearly all of the galaxy images.

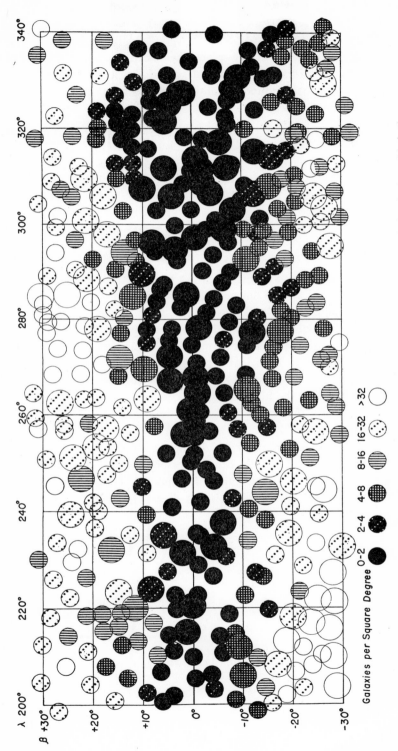

Figure 50. Galaxy population along the southern Milky Way. Coordinates are galactic longitude and latitude.

Galaxies per Square Degree   0-2   2-4   4-8   8-16   16-32   >32

The qualification of the plates has been made on an arbitrary scale that considers the form and size of the stellar images and the nature of the background. Qualities have been reduced to "good" by the following factors:

Quality	Number of Plates	Correction Factor	Quality	Number of Plates	Correction Factor
10	44	1.0	6	34	1.8
9	104	1.0	5	11	2.2
8	141	1.0	4	1	2.6
7	80	1.4			

The correction factors are applied to the galaxy counts.

D. Graphical representation of the opacity

For the construction of Figure 50 we have used the adjusted numbers of galaxies per square degree, $\bar{N}_r$, for the central nine square degrees on each plate (a square 3° on a side). In this central area the magnitudes and nebular counts need no correction for image deformation. For 87 of the plates the coverage has been increased by using the adjusted numbers of galaxies per square degree for the central 21 square degrees (see Fig. 51). This greater coverage was derived only for the plates of the higher qualities centered at declinations south of −27°. North of that declination the fuller survey is left to northern telescopes.

The counts for the outer 12° in these enlarged areas were adjusted for the distance from the center,[3] before they were combined with the $\bar{N}_r$ data for the construction of Figure 50. The shading is heaviest for the areas of greatest opacity. It decreases step-wise as shown by the table.

Average Number of Galaxies per Square Degree	Estimated Absorption[4] in Magnitudes
< 2	> 2.0
4–2	1.5–2.0
8–4	1.0–1.5
16–8	0.5–1.0
32–16	0.0–0.5
> 32	0.0

3. Harlow Shapley and Jacqueline Sweeney, *Proc. Nat. Acad. Sci.*, *41*, 840–1 (1955) (Harv. Reprint 427).
4. In excess of the average in the galactic polar zones.

E. Details of the obscuration

The following tabulation of the galactic coordinates of some of the outstanding objects of the southern Milky Way shows their location with respect to the general obscuration:

	λ	β
NGC 2427 (large spiral) [5]	227°	—12°
Large Magellanic Cloud	247	—33
η Carinae (nebula)	255	0
South celestial pole	270	—28
Coalsack (obscuration)	271	—1
ω Centauri (globular cluster)	277	15
α Centauri	284	—1
VSF 233 ("window")	301	—16
VSF 269 ("window")	307	—20
ρ Ophiuchi (obscuration)	322	—1
Galactic center	328	—1

Within 10° of the Eta Carinae nebulosity are many galaxies. The globular cluster Omega Centauri is apparently obscured to the extent of more than half a magnitude, and its distance should therefore be estimated as somewhat less than 20,000 light years.[6] The Large Magellanic Cloud lies in a region fairly clear of obscuration, or possibly in front of a metagalactic cloud of distant galaxies.

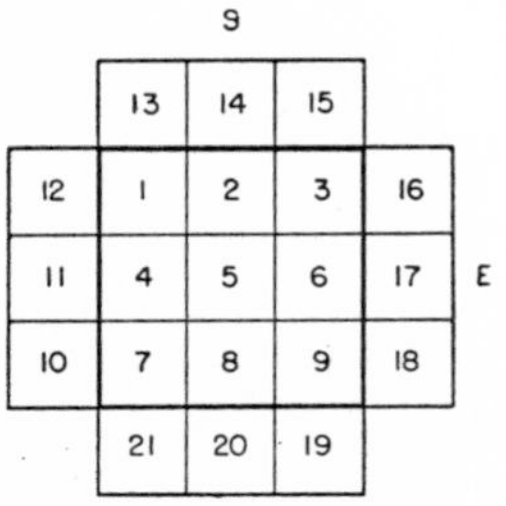

Figure 51.
Diagram of the numbering
in the central
21-square-degree area
of Bruce plates

We now see that the Variable Star Fields 233 and 269, where we have extensively worked on the variable stars, using them as indicators of the distance to the galactic center,[7] are no more free of obscuration than many equally low-latitude areas in the third quadrant of galactic

5. Possibly a nearby heavily obscured spiral; see *Astr. Jour.*, *59*, 169 (1954).
6. *Proc. Nat. Acad. Sci.*, *30*, 67 (1944) (Harv. Reprint 257).
7. *Harv. Circ.*, No. 411 (1936); *Proc. Nat. Acad. Sci.*, *25*, 113 (1939) (Harv. Reprint 158).

longitude; but these other areas, because of their large angular distance from the center, can be of little use in getting its linear distance from the observer.

The Milky Way so far as obscuration is concerned is rather narrow in longitudes 210° to 260° where there are many galaxies with latitudes less than +10°. In this third quadrant the belt of obscuration extends from the galactic circle into negative latitudes a little farther than into positive latitudes, possibly reflecting the position of the observer slightly to the north of the galactic plane, or perhaps indicating the need for an adjustment, of a degree or so, in the adopted position of the galactic poles.

The diagram here presented confirms earlier evidence [8] of a substantial flare of obscuration over most of the south celestial polar zone, declinations −60° to −90°. The affected region is the area between longitudes 250° and 290° and latitude −10° to −30°, where only one plate shows more than 32 galaxies per square degree.

It should be remembered that a shortcoming of all this work, and especially of the attempt to evaluate opacities in small areas, is the necessary assumption of an essentially uniform distribution of galaxies. Clusters and clouds of galaxies are known to exist. One such approaches the galactic equator in longitude 210°, latitude −15°. And the extensive metagalactic cloud of galaxies that appears in the vicinity of the Large Magellanic Cloud apparently extends to latitude −15° in longitude 250°.

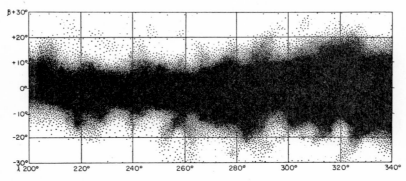

Figure 52. Smoothed representation of the opacity of dust clouds in the southern Milky Way

8. *Harv. Ann.,* *105,* No. 8 (1937).

The apparent abundance of galaxies at λ 320°, $\beta - 15°$, is surprising. The area is less than 20° from the galactic center. The region should be explored with large reflectors to check the apparently high transparency and to apply the galaxy–variable star method to a determination of the distance from the sun to the galactic nucleus.

The Bruce plates used in this survey actually cover the whole area within the bounds of λ 200° to 340°, $\beta +30°$ to $-30°$, but because of image distortion the outer parts of the plates are not dependable enough to be used for the diagrams. The competent coverage, however, is sufficient to justify interpolation over the whole area. In Figure 52 we give the smoothed result. The diagram, which can be taken as a summary of our work on the opacity of the southern Milky Way, should be useful in various investigations. For example, with this survey as a preliminary guide, the relation of interstellar hydrogen, both neutral and ionized, to stars, spiral arms, and obscurations may be more readily studied with radio telescopes than before.

CHAPTER 11. WINDOWS IN THE COSMIC SMOG

A. On the use of galaxies

Three practical uses in astronomical research have been found for the galaxies in addition to their major contribution as fundamental units in our concept of the macrocosmos. They provide a test of the optical quality of a telescope lens or mirror over a large field,[1] although there are better tests, of course; they provide a relatively steady background against which to measure, as at the Lick Observatory, the proper motions of faint galactic stars; and they also supply a background against which to measure the amount of space absorption along the borders of the Milky Way where there is as yet no direct alternative method for finding the *total* obscuration and scattering by interstellar dust.

The degree of transparency in a given low-latitude field is estimated, as shown in the preceding chapter for the southern Milky Way, by the average number of galaxies per square degree in that field compared with the numbers in relatively clear high-latitude regions. Color excess produced by interstellar light-scattering material is also a test of transparency, but methods involving measures of the color of galaxies have not yet been well developed and they may remain of low accuracy because of the considerable inherent diversity in the natural colors of galaxies. Some are as blue as Class A stars, others are yellowish with integrated spectra of Class G and later. Photoelectric color photometry, such as that developed by Stebbins and Whitford[2] and by Pettit,[3] gives the highest promise for the quantitative measure of space absorption when the types of the galaxies involved are accurately known.

A related service of galaxies is connected with the most important use of the cluster type cepheids, for an abundance of low-latitude

1. Harlow Shapley and Rebecca B. Jones, *Proc. Nat. Acad. Sci.*, 26, 556 (1940) (Harv. Reprint 208).
2. *Astroph. Jour.*, 108, 413–28 (1948) (*Mt. Wilson Contr.*, No. 753)
3. *Astroph. Jour.*, 120, 413–38 (1954).

galaxies will indicate areas of high transparency where the magnitudes of the cepheids may lead to reliable measures of the distance to the center and the dimensions of the galactic system. The galaxy-cepheid method is illustrated later in this chapter.

B. The borders of the Milky Way

The character of the Zone of Obscuration along the southern Milky Way is indicated by the diagrams of the preceding chapter. Less can be reported as yet on the Milky Way borders in the northern sky. Along the whole course of the Milky Way the diagrams in Chapter 3 show a region 20° wide that is empty of galaxies brighter than magnitude 12.9. For fainter galaxies the zone naturally is irregularly narrower, as shown by figures in Chapters 7, 8, and 10.

The reason for variation in the width and opacity of the Zone of Obscuration is not far to seek. The arms of our spiral galaxy are of different dimensions, differently affected by dust clouds, and possibly differently inclined [4] to the median galactic plane. The Zone, as indicated in the surveys by Mount Wilson for the north and by Harvard for the south, is widest in the fourth quadrant (galactic center) and narrowest in galactic longitudes 35°, 105°, 210°, and 265°. Hubble's chart of nebular distribution for the northern sky is reproduced in Figure 37; the supplementary Harvard charts for the southern Milky Way are shown in Chapter 10.

The most transparent of the low-latitude regions we have called "windows." If when working through a window we find faint cepheid variable stars to be numerous, we can use them to estimate the extent of the Milky Way discoid in the direction of the window; we can also explore the outlying corona of distant stars, described in a later chapter. In particular, as mentioned above, we can use this cepheid-and-galaxy method as an effective way of finding the distance to the galactic center. This distance is an important metagalactic parameter which is also evaluated through the analysis of galactic rotation (Oort, Lindblad), the two-color study of variable stars near the galactic nucleus (Baade, Gaposchkin), the distribution of emission nebulae (Morgan,

4. For an example of the inclination of a substructure of our galaxy, see the evidence of an inclined "local system" of faint B and A stars reported in *Harvard Circular*, No. 229 (1922) and Harvard Reprint 6 (1924). For naked-eye stars the Gould Belt is an indication of this inclined flattened structure in our part of the galactic system.

Bok, and colleagues), the distribution and motion of the 21-centimeter radiation of neutral hydrogen (Leiden Observatory), and by the method used first of all, that is, by the distribution in space of the globular clusters.

Five of the windows where faint variable stars have been found are described in the following pages. Some of them are more than 10° from the galactic circle and hardly qualify as windows. They do, however, register a break in the dust barrier and may be instructively associated with the spiral structure of the Milky Way. In the preceding chapter on the dust and gas of the southern Milky Way, attention is called to the narrowness of the Milky Way dust clouds in the third quadrant of galactic longitude. There for an interval of 60° in longitude on both sides of the Milky Way galaxies are found within the ±10° latitude belt. The bearing of this feature on galactic structure may be revealed soon by the radio telescopes.

C. Southern windows

1. VSF 233. Several years of work at the telescopes and at plate measuring frames have been devoted to the securing of more than 25,000 magnitude estimates for a field in the constellations of Pavo and Ara on the edge of the southern Milky Way. This region, which bears the designation VSF 233, is one of the several hundred numbered fields covering the sky that were set up at the Harvard Observatory many years ago for the systematic study of variable stars. In the southern hemisphere each field covers 70 to 100 square degrees; in the northern 35 to 50 square degrees, and VSF 233 is one of the 50 or so that have now received special and sometimes prolonged investigation.

The special attraction of VSF 233 lies in its richness in faint galaxies, uncommon for a low-latitude region, and its richness also in faint and distant variable stars of all sorts. One corner of the field is but 10° from the galactic circle, and 26° from the galactic center. The coordinnates of the center of the field are

$$\text{R.A.} = 17^h\ 36^m\ \text{Decl.} = -59°$$
$$\lambda = 301°\qquad \beta = -16°.$$

In Chapter 2 a preliminary reference is made to VSF 233, and it will be mentioned again when we discuss the distance and coordinates of the galactic center. Here we shall give a distribution diagram and a bibliography of this interesting region which undoubtedly will be further explored with the larger telescopes of the southern hemisphere. Figure 53 shows the distribution of galaxies and of three major kinds of variable stars, as explained in the legend. The variable star population is divided as follows: cluster type, 59; eclipsing, 41; long-period, 79; irregular, etc., 28; total 207.

The area covered by the diagram is close to 100 square degrees and in it 717 galaxies are identified. The average space absorption, corresponding to a population of only seven galaxies per square degree, is about 1.25 magnitudes more than that in the polar zones.

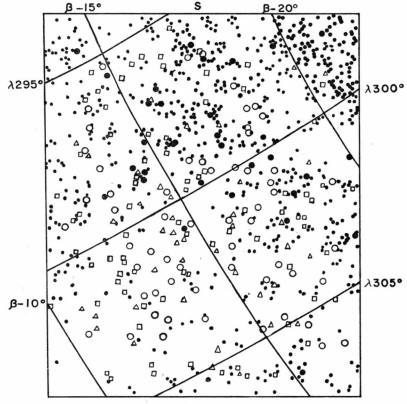

Figure 53. Distribution of variables and galaxies in VSF 233. Large filled circles, galaxies brighter than 15.1; small filled circles, galaxies fainter than 15.0. Open circles, cluster type variables; open squares, long-period variables; open triangles, eclipsing binaries

The grouping of the brighest galaxies in the several square degrees around λ 298°, β −16°, may indicate the existence there of a loose organization at a distance of perhaps ten megaparsecs. The high frequency of galaxies in the upper right corner of the diagram may be associated with the metagalactic cloud of galaxies that is shown on other plates around longitude 300°, latitude −25° to −40°.

It is noteworthy that variables of all three principal types are intermingled with galaxies in all parts of the field; but in the lower left quadrant there is a scarcity of galaxies. The low quality of the Bruce plates used for this section of the field is partly responsible for the small number of galaxies, but we are here approaching the Milky Way dust clouds. Only one cluster type variable is found nearer to the galactic circle than −11°.

2. Exploring beyond the galactic center. Some of the cluster variable stars of VSF 233 must be as distant from us as is the center of the Milky Way. To go further through this window Miss Boyd and the writer studied a special series of Bruce plates made at the South African station of the Harvard Observatory. They cover only the central 30 square degrees of VSF 233, but they reach two magnitudes fainter and have provided 190 new variables of which 136 are of the useful cluster type. (This series of plates was designed in such a way that cluster variables would be easily discovered whereas other types would not be so readily brought to light.) In this deeper reach we have gone to distances of about fifteen megaparsecs for variables fainter then the 17th magnitude, and for the first time have definitely entered the far side of the large galactic nucleus.[5] The new material becomes useful in estimating the distance to the galactic center and will be briefly discussed in Chapter 12.

Referring again to the abundance of galaxies recorded through this southern window, we observe that it does not necessarily follow that the space absorption in the clearer parts of VSF 233 is negligible. It may be that a cloud of distant galaxies covers practically all of this region and that unreckoned absorption has brought the population

5. Subsequently in other fields we have by-passed the galactic nucleus, and recently Baade and S. Gaposchkin have done the same in a field near the center, using color excess rather than galaxy background to estimate the necessary corrections for absorption. Walter Baade, *Pub. Obs. Mich., 10,* 16 (1951); stenciled lecture notes, Michigan Symposium on Astrophysics, pp. 23–7 (1953).

back to what we observe. Here we shall adopt, for the later computation of the distance to the galactic center, a total absorption of 1.5 magnitudes—a value that includes the assumed residual absorption 0.25 magnitude in the galactic polar zones.

The galaxies of VSF 233 and its neighborhood, and the absorption problems, are treated in detail in *Harvard Circular,* No. 411 (1936), where the forms and diameters of the faint galaxies are also examined. The principal communications that concern the field are the following:

Harvard Bulletin, No. 901 (1935) by Shapley
Harvard Annals, 90, No. 7 (1935) by Henrietta H. Swope
Harvard Circular, No. 411 (1936) by Shapley
Harvard Annals, 105, No. 13 (1936) by Shapley and Constance D. Boyd
Harvard Bulletin, No. 904 (1936) by Shapley

3. The Centaurus window. Across the Milky Way from VSF 233 is the 8th magnitude spiral, *NGC* 4945, which is only 12° from the galactic circle and is naturally somewhat faint in surface brightness. Its elliptical dimensions are 18′ by 3.′5. Actually it may be a flattened Magellanic type galaxy on edge. It is surrounded by a considerable number of faint galaxies, which suggests a region of fair transparency. VSF 298 covers the region adequately. On a 30-minute ADH plate [6] covering 17.5 square degrees, Miss Hearn has marked over 200 galaxies. In this central portion of VSF 298 they occur at the rate of 12.1 per square degree to magnitude 17.8. The corresponding absorption is approximately 0.8 magnitude compared with that observed in the high-latitude sky. The field should be of value in finding the extension of the Milky Way discoid and its corona in the Centaurus direction, for on a series of ADH plates suitable for variable star discovery 46 new variables, not all of them definitely confirmed, have been found by Pedro Kokaras within the 17.5 square degree field. Previously known in the whole VSF 298 area are 59 variable stars according to the Kukarkin and Parenago catalogue, half of which were found by W. J. Luyten in the course of his proper-motion work with Harvard plates. The whole field merits detailed study.

6. The plates made with the Baker-Schmidt reflector at the Boyden Station of the Harvard Observatory are designated ADH (Armagh-Dunsink-Harvard).

4. VSF 187. The galaxies recorded nearest to the galactic center probably are those that appear in one section of the 80-square-degree field of VSF 187, centered at λ 322°5, β —7°5, where Miss Swope has discovered about 700 new variable stars. The field is adjacent to VSF 190, which contains the globular cluster *NGC* 6522 around which Baade and Gaposchkin have made their study of faint cluster variables for the determination of the distance from the sun to the galactic center. In one part of the field, around the position λ 320°, β —10°5 (only 11°5 from the galactic center) the galaxies to magnitude 17.7 average about five per square degree. With the usual caution about localized deviations from the average population of galaxies and about the magnitude scales, we compute that the total space absorption is 1.35 magnitudes. The maximum frequency of median magnitudes of cluster variables, in the area where the faint galaxies are found, is 16.0. From this value and the galactic coordinates we compute the distance from the sun to the galactic center as 7.8 kiloparsecs, a value that later will be compared with results from other fields.

The region of VSF 187 should yield rich returns for the future investigator of variable stars and of low-latitude space absorption in the galactic nucleus. Some parts of the field are completely blacked out as far as translucent galaxies are concerned; other parts seem to be moderately well populated. The survey for variables by Miss Swope [7] does not nearly exhaust the discoveries possible on existing Harvard plates; probably 2,000 variables can be found brighter than the 18th magnitude and 20,000 brighter than the 20th.

From the study of 239 variables in one-third of the field Miss Swope finds that all types are present:

	Cluster	Cepheid	Eclipsing	Long-period	Irregular
Per cent	31	1	5	44	17

Occasionally novae are found. In another third of the field the above percentages are approximately maintained, but for variable stars fainter than the magnitude limit in Miss Swope's study, and nearer the galactic center, Baade and S. Gaposchkin find that the percentage of cluster variables is greatly increased.

VSF 185, which lies across the Milky Way from VSF 187 (λ =

7. Henrietta H. Swope, *Harv. Ann., 90,* 215–29 (1935), and *Harv. Ann., 109,* No. 10 (1943).

322.5, $\beta = +7.5$), is rich in faint variable stars but devoid of galaxies. It too has been studied by Miss Swope. From the cluster variables the writer has computed a distance of 8.0 kiloparsecs from the sun to the galactic center, but the determination is of negligible weight because of uncertain allowance for intervening space absorption. It is quite possible that these variables are chiefly at the nearer edge of the central galactic spheroid.

5. *VSF 269 and the galactic nucleus.* The field that is centered at λ 307°, β −20°, can scarcely qualify as a window in the sense of being a low-latitude break in the cosmic smog. It is, however, near enough the galactic center to be rich in cluster variables while at the same time well populated with external galaxies; [8] it therefore has a valuable contribution to make to galactic dimensions. A long series of MF plates (10-inch Metcalf camera) covers the 80-square-degree field adequately for the discovery and analysis of the variable stars. To locate the galaxies and estimate their magnitudes we have used ten long-exposure Bruce plates (scale: 1 mm = 1′). Plate qualities vary considerably but there is much overlap and we are confident that the galaxy survey is fairly complete to the 18th magnitude. Certainly down to magnitude 17.4 the frequency of galaxies can be used satisfactorily to judge the degree of space transparency.

The distribution of stars and galaxies is fairly even over VSF 269. The numbers of the latter in the four quadrants are 149, 166, 174, and 179. The following tabulation gives the number of galaxies down to and including various magnitude limits:

To magnitude	15.0	15.6	16.05	16.5	17.0	17.4
Number	25	53	82	129	281	542

Following the usual method, where N is the number of galaxies per square degree to the obversed magnitude m', and m_1 is the space-density parameter, which is the magnitude reach necessary to have on the average one galaxy per square degree, we compute the total photographic space absorption in magnitudes from the relation

$$\Delta m = m' - m_1 - 1.67 \log N$$

and for $m_1 = 15.2$ (from Chapter 5) get the following results:

8. Harlow Shapley, Emily H. Boyce, and Constance D. Boyd, *Harv. Ann.,* *90,* No. 9 (1939); cf. also *Proc. Nat. Acad. Sci., 25,* 113–18 (1939) (Harv. Reprint 158).

m'	15.0	15.6	16.05	16.5	17.0	17.4
N	0.31	0.66	1.02	1.61	3.51	6.78
Δm	0.65	0.69	0.83	0.95	0.89	0.81
Weight	1	2	2	2	1	1

The weighted mean value of the absorption, 0.81 magnitude, is subject, of course, to the assumption that the magnitude scale and the adopted space-density parameter m_1 are reasonably good. All the cluster variables of VSF 269 lie at distances from the galactic plane, $r \sin \beta$, greater than a kiloparsec. It is reasonable, therefore, to assume that the detected space absorption is between the observer and the variable stars (that it is, in fact, in the neighborhood of the sun). Therefore Δm can be treated as a zero point correction to the magnitude scale, the same for all variables of VSF 269 whatever their magnitudes and distances.

Of the more than 500 variable stars in VSF 269, 300 are cluster type cepheids. For greater security with the magnitudes, we have used in computing distances only the 77 variables in the central twenty square degrees, where the survey has been uniformly carried to the workable limit of the Bruce plates. The frequencies of median magni-

Table 11. Frequency of Median Magnitudes

Magnitude Interval	Number of Variables	Corrected Mean Magnitude
12.5–12.9	1	11.85
13.0–13.4	2	12.10
13.5–13.9	2	12.70
14.0–14.4	7	13.29
14.5–14.9	16	13.77
15.0–15.4	27	14.25
15.5–15.9	16	14.70
16.0–16.4	5	15.15
16.5–16.9	1	15.55

tudes are shown in Table 11. The mean median magnitudes in the third column have been corrected for the 0.8 magnitude absorption indicated by the galaxy population, and corrected also for the residual general absorption of 0.25 now commonly assumed for the galactic polar zones to which our m_1 refers. The maximum frequency of medians comes at observed apparent magnitude 15.3. Corrected for absorption it is at 14.25. If we are right in assuming that the cluster variables are concentrated symmetrically toward the center of the galactic spheroids, this is the value that should enter (in Chapter 12) in the computation of the distance of the galactic center from the sun.[9]

D. A window in Perseus

Along the northern Milky Way are a few breaks in the dust clouds of singular interest. In galactic longitudes 30° to 40° (Vulpecula and Cygnus) the galaxies crowd into low latitudes on both sides of the galactic circle. A few degrees to the north through a transparent spot in Cygnus (λ 44°, β +5°), the famous discrete radio source, Cygnus A, was found. Later it was identified by Baade, using the Hale reflector, with a pair of dimly photographed, faint, and very remote galaxies which are apparently "in collision."

In Perseus a well known cluster of faint galaxies lies in latitude −13°. The brightest object in the group is *NGC* 1275, a radio source that has received much attention, for here again may be interpenetrating galaxies [10] where the turbulent interstellar gas and dust clouds provide the radio signals. Not only is the rather compact cluster of galaxies found in this low latitude, but a number of field galaxies are present. The space absorption in the neighborhood must be relatively light. VSF 299 covers the region, and on MC plates (16-inch Metcalf) which cover about 30 square degrees effectively Miss Hearn has marked several suspected variables. When the cluster variables have been identified and their magnitudes determined, we shall have a good indication of the extent of the galaxy in the anti-center direction. In Chapter 13, § A, the extent has been provisionally estimated on the basis of variables and galaxies in neighboring anti-center fields.

9. For the computation appearing in Harvard Reprint 158, we omitted the correction for the residual absorption at the galactic poles. The correction is necessary to reduce to dust-free space. Also we took $m_1 = 15.4$ instead of the better value 15.2. The methods used in that paper are appropriate, but the new values of Δm and m_1 change considerably the deduced distance to the galactic center.

10. W. Baade and R. Minkowski, *Astroph. Jour., 119,* 215–31 (1954); J. E. Baldwin and B. Elsmore, *Nature, 173,* 818–20 (1954).

CHAPTER 12. THE CENTER OF THE MILKY WAY

The heliocentric description of the solar system carried with it for more than three centuries a heliocentric interpretation of the sidereal system. For the students of astronomy there were some rather telling observations to support the view that the sun is at or near the center of the stellar structure, and this support was in addition to the natural but unscientific human desire to adorn oneself with the dignity of a favored position in the universe. The Milky Way does not seem to be conspicuously asymmetrical, as it presumably would appear to a peripheral or even an eccentric observer. The rich central star clouds in Scorpio, Ophiuchus, and Sagittarius would stand out very brilliantly, and long ago would have given the secret away, if it were not for the heavy absorption by interstellar dust which brings the Sagittarius star clouds (for northern hemisphere observers) down to a brightness not much more than that in Cygnus and other parts of the Milky Way. Also the Milky Way band is nearly a great circle, which definitely places the sun very near the mid-plane of the Galaxy, even if not in the center. A further reason for assuming a central position for the sun and the earth came from the analysis of early star counts; there appeared to be a falling off in population with increasing distance from the sun, suggesting of course a central location for us among the stars. This wrong conclusion was partly due to the imperfections in the census, partly to the effects of uneven space absorption, and partly to the fact, for which we now have some good evidence, that we are located near the edge of a spiral arm and at least in some directions there actually is a falling off in stellar population with increasing distance. The outline of the stellar system generally accepted prior to 1915 is illustrated in Figure 13 of Chapter 4.

A. Its direction

The application of the period-luminosity relation of cepheid variables to the determination of the distances of globular star clusters gave us a definite intimation that the heliocentric hypothesis of the sidereal system must be abandoned. The early lists of these peculiar clusters, for example the Messier catalogue, had shown their uneven scattering over the sky. But without knowing their nature or distance astronomers could not usefully speculate on the existence or meaning of an over-all system of globular clusters. The period-luminosity relation, however, led to knowledge of the distances of those that contain cluster type cepheids. Other methods of distance measurement were explored. The apparent magnitudes of the brighter stars gave approximate distances for clusters in which variables had not been found, and rough estimates for the faint unresolved clusters could be based on the integrated apparent magnitudes and on the apparent diameters. In low latitudes where interstellar dust interferes the originally estimated distances (1917) were uncertain, and even now remain so. But for the 30 clusters in intermediate and high latitudes the distances determined in 1917 have been little changed through later investigations.[1]

The revision of the period-luminosity relation in 1953, which has more than doubled the earlier values of the distances of outside galaxies, has left the distances of the globular clusters unaffected for they are based on cluster type cepheids for which the original determination of the median absolute magnitude, $M = 0.0$, has been reinforced through several investigations of various kinds. The newer evaluations of space absorption also have little affected most of the measures of distance for clusters with $\beta > \pm 20°$.

The uncertainties in the earlier distances for low-latitude globular clusters have had no bearing on the determination of the direction of the center of the Galaxy. The position in the sky, not the distances, is the relevant coordinate. To find the direction we first had to use the *New General* and *Index Catalogues* and several photographic surveys for the identification of the globular clusters, which had to be separated from the rich open clusters within the galactic system and from the outside spheroidal galaxies. The positions of the 69 clusters accepted as globular in 1917 were plotted on a map of the total sky. Three interesting facts stood out: first, the globular clusters are almost wholly in one-half of the sky; second, they are concentrated toward a point in the southern Milky Way with coordinates approximately R.A. $17^h 30^m$, Decl. $-30°$, λ 325°, β $-28°$; and third, the Milky Way

1. *Proc. Nat. Acad. Sci., 30,* 61–8 (1944). See also W. Lohmann, *Zeitschrift f. Astroph., 30,* 234–47 (1952).

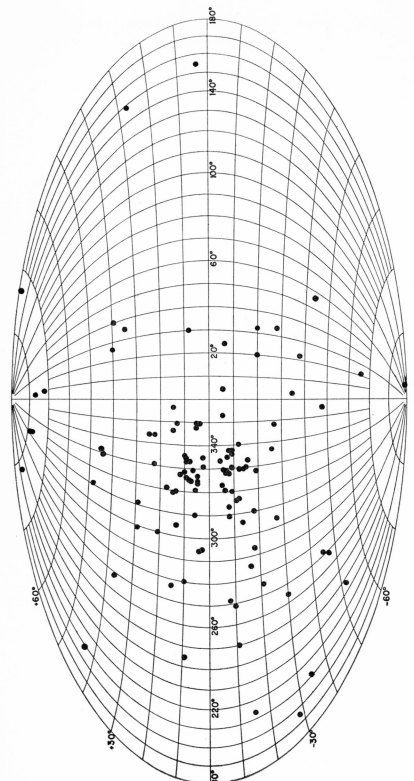

Figure 54. Distribution in galactic coordinates of the 108 globular clusters now recognized as members of our galactic system

plane is fundamental in the over-all system of globular clusters, for the same number are found on each side.

Actually the space distribution of the globular clusters can give us the direction and distance only to the center of the over-all system of globular clusters—not to the center of our spiral galaxy. From the first, however, we have assumed that the centers of the stellar system and of the globular cluster system are the same. We have assumed that if there were a galactic discoid, and a series of spiral arms, and a corona of high-latitude "escape" stars, each would be more or less symmetrically arranged about a nuclear point, and that point is the one located by the globular clusters. There has been no objection to that hypothesis, and increasing support has come from the distribution of stars of various sorts as well as from the dynamics of the system as revealed by galactic rotation. Also from the distribution of neutral hydrogen as uncovered by the radio telescopes has come confirmation. The coordinates of the direction of the center (longitude between 325° and 330°, latitude between 0° and −2°) are agreed upon by globular clusters, galactic rotation, and the radio signals in both neutral hydrogen radiation and in the longer wave lengths.

It is somewhat surprising that the galactic longitude of the direction to the center remains after many and varied investigations close to where it was put in the first plotting in 1917 of the longitudes of 69 globular clusters.[2] The latitude too remains within a degree or two of the galactic circle. But the distance to the center, derived in the early work on clusters, was overestimated because of the neglect, which at that time seemed reasonable, of space absorption. The uncertainty in the distance coordinate was recognized at the time that the direction to the center was fixed.

The number of globular clusters now known in our Galaxy, including some that have been found through red photography penetrating the dust in the nuclear region, has increased from 69 to 106. In Figure 54 a plot of the distribution over the sky emphasizes the concentration toward a center in Sagittarius. Figure 55 shows the frequency of longitudes. From it we derive λ 328° for the longitude of the center of the globular cluster assemblage. The uncertainty can scarcely be more than a degree or two. New discoveries in the star and dust clouds of Scorpio, Sagittarius, and Ophiuchus are not likely to displace this central longitude appreciably.

2. *Mt. Wilson Contr.*, No. 152 (1918), Fig. 3.

The globular clusters yield a less precise value for the latitude of the center. In Figure 56 we plot the frequency of latitudes, and derive $\beta_c = -1°0$. Discoveries of new globular clusters might shift this value by half a degree or so.

The center as derived from radio has been variously measured. Some recent results, summarized by Kraus and Ko, are given in Table 12.[3] There can be little doubt that the stars, clusters, and the radio sources are referring to the same nuclear point. The negative latitude is presumably the reflection of the observer's position a hundred light years or so north of the galactic plane.

The direction coordinates obtained by other methods,[4] such as the

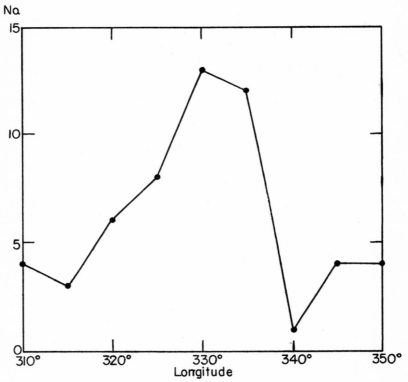

Figure 55. Distribution of globular clusters in galactic longitude. Only those with latitudes less than ±40° and longitudes 310° to 350° are included.

3. J. D. Kraus and H. C. Ko, *Ohio Radio Obs. Report*, No. 1 (1954).

4. J. H. Oort, *Astroph. Jour.*, 116, 237 (1952). See also *Bul. Ast. Inst. Neth.*, 12, 133 (1954).

analysis of galactic rotation, star counts, and color excesses, and the distribution of H II regions and of special types of stars such as novae, are all consistent with the values indicated by globular clusters and radio sources.

B. Its distance

As mentioned above, the distribution in space of globular clusters is not a good guide to the distance to the galactic center. The corrections for space absorption in low latitudes are still uncertain, and the census

Table 12. Position of the Galactic Nucleus (Radio Measures)

Observer	Wave Length (cm)	λ	β
Haddock, Mayer, and Sloanaker	9.4	327°62	—1°46
Haddock	3	327.70	—1.40
Hagen and McClain *	21	327.90	—1.41
Kraus and Ko	120	327.81	—1.42
McGee and Bolton	75	327.9	—1.
van de Hulst, Muller, and Oort	21	328.0	—1.5
Most probable position		327.79	—1.39

* In a later report McClain gives the values λ 327°8, β —1°4 (*Astroph. Jour.*, *122*, 376–84 [1955]), but suggests that his measures may refer to a radio source this side of the nucleus.

of globular clusters in our galactic system is undoubtedly incomplete, especially in the trans-center part of the Milky Way. Edmondson has estimated that the total number of globular clusters may be in the

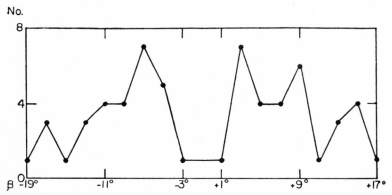

Figure 56. Distribution in galactic latitude of globular clusters of the fourth quadrant. Those in latitudes higher than ± 20° are not plotted.

neighborhood of 200;[5] and although this is not an important argument, the number in the similar giant Sb spiral, Messier 31, is about the same.

Estimates of the distance to the center based on measures and analyses of galactic rotation involve assumptions that lower confidence in the precision of the results,[6] but from the distribution and motions of the neutral hydrogen clouds van de Hulst, Muller, and Oort have obtained a value of $d_g = 8.26$ kpc.[7] Baade and Gaposchkin, as mentioned in Chapter 11, have made an extensive study of the cluster variables in a small field centered on globular cluster *NGC* 6522 in Sagittarius, a few degrees from the galactic center. The most frequent median magnitude is found to be 17.3. Applying a correction of 2.75 magnitudes for intervening space absorption, a value based on very careful photoelectric work on Selected Area 68 by Stebbins and Whitford which permitted the derivation of color excesses for the globular cluster and for some of the variable stars, Baade [8] derives a distance to the center of $d_g = 8.16$ kpc. Much earlier the writer and colleagues at the Harvard Observatory had used this method of measuring d_g, but instead of estimating the absorption from the color excesses we used the background of galaxies as an indicator of the degree of transparency (cf. preceding chapter). Both methods have basic uncertainties, the former with the usual errors inherent in color photometry and faint magnitude sequences, the latter with the magnitude sequences and the intrinsic unevenness in the distribution of faint galaxies.

Neither the Leiden nor the Mount Wilson workers have published a calculated probable error of the estimates of distance d_g, but 0.4 kpc appears to be a reasonable suggestion. Perhaps 0.6 kpc is better in view of the sensitive factors involved. For example, in Baade's deduction an error of one-tenth of a magnitude, either in the adopted space absorption of 2.75 magnitudes or in the apparent median magnitude of the most frequent cluster variable, produces an error of nearly 0.4 kpc in his value of $d_g = 8.16$.

5. Frank K. Edmondson, *Ast. Jour.*, *45*, 13 (1935).

6. Harold Weaver, *Ast. Jour.*, *60*, 181 (1955).

7. H. C. van de Hulst, C. A. Muller, and J. H. Oort, *Bul. Ast. Inst. Neth.*, *12*, 117 (1954).

8. Michigan Symposium on Astrophysics (1953).

C. Measures dependent on the cepheid-galaxy method

Chapter 11 referred to a revision of the determination of d_g based on the cluster variables in VSF 269. Fuller details of the procedure are given in Harvard Reprint 158 (1939). The value of d_g first determined seventeen years ago [9] has been revised downward through an allowance of 0.25 magnitude for assumed space absorption in the galactic polar zones, and by using the revised value 15.2 for the space-density parameter (instead of 15.4). In the photometric determinations of d_g at Harvard and Mount Wilson we have made a reasonable assumption that the cluster variables are symmetrically concentrated to the center of the central spheroid in which they are found. If they are concentrated off center we are correspondingly misled.

Low weight values of d_g have also been determined for two other low-latitude variable star fields on the edge of the central spheroid, VSF 187 and VSF 233 (Chapter 11). The data for these are not sufficient for a reliable determination of the maximum frequency of median magnitudes for the cluster variables. From the three variable star fields we have:

VSF	Weight	d_g
269	4	7.9 kpc
233	1	9.2
187	1	7.8
Mean		8.15

The close agreement of the mean with the Leiden value of 8.26 and the Mount Wilson value of 8.16 is accidental since its probable error must be of the order of 0.4 kpc. Further revision of all three values is possible and probable, though laborious. For the present it appears that we should accept for the distance of the sun from the galactic center

$$d_g = 8.2 \text{ kpc} = 26,700 \text{ light years,}$$

with a probable error of about 500 parsecs or 1,600 light years. In 1956 the problem is receiving renewed attention by several investigators.

9. *Proc. Nat. Acad. Sci.*, **25**, 113–18 (1939) (Harv. Reprint 158).

CHAPTER 13. ON THE DIAMETERS
OF THE GALACTIC
SYSTEM

The preceding chapter indicates that 8.2 ± 0.5 kiloparsecs is a fair value, in keeping with present evidence, for the distance from the sun to the galactic center. The further application of the galaxy-cepheid method of estimating sidereal distance in and near the Milky Way has made possible a preliminary estimate of the extent of the galactic system in the anti-center region, and therefore an estimate of the total diameter. For the work on the variables and galaxies in the anti-center area we have chosen the bounds

galactic latitude +40° to −40°,
galactic longtitude 110° to 180°,

an area which encompasses 5,000 square degrees (one-eighth of the sky). The investigation is far from complete, but in order to contribute what we can to knowledge of the dimensions of a giant galaxy, and to assist the explorations of the galactic dust and gas clouds now under way with radio telescopes the results at present available are summarized in this chapter.

A. Cluster cepheids of the anti-center

Approximately a hundred cluster type variables are now known in the anti-center area, of which the great majority were found on Harvard plates. When sufficiently observed the distances in kiloparsecs have been computed from the usual relation

$$d = 10^{0.2(\dot{m}_0 - \Delta m - \dot{M}) - 2},\qquad(1)$$

where $\dot{m}_0$ is the observed median magnitude derived from the light curve and Δm is the space absorption (light scattering) in magnitudes between observer and star. By adopting the usual value of the median absolute photographic magnitude, $M = 0$, and introducing the corrected median apparent magnitude,

$$\dot{m}_c = \dot{m}_0 - \Delta m,\qquad(2)$$

we have from (1)

$$\log d = 0.2 \dot{m}_c - 2.$$

The distance of a variable star from the galactic plane, its distance from the observer projected on the center–anti-center line in the galactic plane, and the distance from the center of the galaxy to the star, are given respectively by

$$z = d \sin \beta, \tag{3}$$
$$w = d \cos \beta \cos (\lambda - 145°), \tag{4}$$
$$d_g = [z^2 + s^2 + (d \cos \beta)^2 + 2sw]^{1/2}, \tag{5}$$

where β and λ are the galactic coordinates, the longitude of the galactic center is taken as 325°, and s is the distance from the observer to the galactic center. For the following computations we have used $s = 8.3$ kpc.

The coverage of the anti-center region with long-exposure plates for the detection of faint galaxies has been completed. Two Agassiz Station telescopes, the 16-inch Metcalf and the 24-33-inch Jewett-Schmidt, have contributed most of the long-exposure photographs. Nearly all the shorter-exposure plates for the discovery and study of variable stars are made with the Metcalf instrument.

From the counts of galaxies on the long-exposure plates to magnitude m_o, we derive the absorption Δm from the equation that connects numbers of galaxies per square degree, N, with apparent magnitudes:

$$\log N = b(m_o - \Delta m - m_1).$$

Adopting $b = 0.6$, $m_1 = 15.2$, as parameters for uniformly distributed population comparable with that in the galactic polar zones, we have

$$\Delta m = m_o - 15.2 - 1.67 \log \bar{N},$$

where for each plate m_o is the observed faintest magnitude for galaxy images. From this relation we compute the absorption and proceed first to the determination of m_c from (2) and then, from the galactic coordinates and equations (3), (4), and (5), to the derivation of distances d_g for the 52 stars in Table 13.

For 32 additional cluster variables the galaxies in the area surrounding them are so few, faint, and uncertain that no attempt has been made to evaluate the absorption and distances. For ten stars in Table 13, where the absorption is one magnitude or greater, the distances are necessarily uncertain and the tabulated values are marked with colons. The brightest cluster variables are of course relatively near. We cannot be sure, in the absence of accurate measures of color, whether such variables are actually beyond the absorbing material, or in it, or in front. (This indecision applies also to many of the 65 classical cepheids in the region, which we do not use because of their low latitudes or their relatively small distances.) If the variables are in the light scattering dust, or in front, we have overcorrected the magnitudes for absorption. But for all the regions with β greater than $\pm 10°$ we can assume safely that the faint variables lie far beyond the absorption, and the full value of Δm computed from the galaxy counts should be applied.

We have, of course, recognized the possibility that the average galaxy population in the galactic polar zones, to which we have reduced the anti-center galaxy counts, is affected by some absorption; therefore, for all of the variable star magnitudes in the anti-center octant we have applied a further correction of 0.25 magnitude to whatever absorption is indicated by the scarcity of faint galaxies along the Milky Way. This correction has decreased all distances computed without it by 11 per cent.

The median magnitudes of the variable stars and the plate limits for the galaxy survey are based on various magnitude standards, including Selected Area Sequences and, for the higher-latitude fields, sequences set up through star counts and the Seares and van Rhijn tables. The magnitude standards are of course subject to the usual uncertainties of photographic photometry, but the errors probably average out; in any case, because of the inescapable uncertainties in the correction for space absorption, such errors may be neglected in this qualitative investigation.

In estimating the absorption, Δm, we have assumed that the true population of background galaxies in the anti-center octant, when freed of interstellar absorption, is comparable with the average population for the high-latitude sky. To the extent that this assumption fails, through significant irregularities in the distribution of faint galaxies, the individual distances are uncertain. But the general order of the distances, we believe, is dependably estimated, and therefore

Table 13. Fifty-Two Variables in the Anti-center Octant

Name	Period	β	λ	Δm	$\dot{m}_c$	d(kpc)	z(kpc)	d_g(kpc)
RX Eri	0.5872	−32	181	0.25	8.95	0.6	−0.3	8.7
X Ari	0.6511	−38	137	0.25	9.0	0.6	−0.4	8.8
BC Eri	0.2639	−33	179	0.25	10.0	1.0	−0.5	9.0
RR Gem	0.3973	+21	155	0.9	10.65	1.4	+0.5	9.6
TT Cnc	0.5634	+29	180	0.25	11.10	1.7	+0.8	9.6
SZ Gem	0.5011	+24	170	0.3	10.9	1.5	+0.6	9.6
AH Tau	0.1663	−22	135	1.0	10.85:	1.5:	−0.6:	9.7:
48.1933 *	....	−21	130	1.5	11.0:	1.6:	−0.6:	9.8:
SS Tau	0.3700	−37	147	1.0	11.25:	1.8:	−1.1:	9.8:
TZ Aur	0.3917	+22	145	0.5	11.15	1.7	+0.6	9.9
SS Cnc	0.3673	+28	167	0.55	11.4	1.9	+0.9	9.9
RV Ari	0.0852	−40	117	0.35	11.85	2.3	−1.5	10.0
RW Ari	0.2614	−40	117	0.35	12.05	2.6	−1.6	10.2
TY Cam	0.6701	+16	117	1.5	11.7:	2.2:	+0.6:	10.2:
44.1929 *	....	−23	170	0.45	11.8	2.3	−0.9	10.3
HV 7668 *	....	+20	139	0.8	11.95	2.5	+0.8	10.6
RZ Cam	0.4804	+24	115	0.3	12.3	2.9	+1.2	10.7
XY Eri	0.5542	−40	174	0.25	12.85	3.7	−2.4	11.1
SX Cnc	....	+38	168	0.25	12.8	3.6	+2.2	11.2
HV 10389	....	−24	155	0.8	12.5	3.2	−1.3	11.2
HV 7649 *	....	+17	136	1.5	12.5:	3.2:	+0.9:	11.3:
GP Aur	....	+15	138	1.5	12.5:	3.2:	+0.8:	11.4:
HV 7661 *	....	+20	136	1.0	12.55:	3.2:	+1.1:	11.4:
YZ Tau	0.4115	−22	135	1.0	12.70:	3.5:	−1.3:	11.6:
CR Aur	0.5914	+16	138	1.5	12.85:	3.7:	+1.0:	11.9:
BE Eri	0.5795	−29	166	0.25	13.15	4.3	−2.1	12.0
AL Eri	0.6569	−38	180	0.25	13.6	5.2	−3.2	12.4
CV Tau	....	−24	137	0.9	13.2	4.4	−1.8	12.4
AC Eri	0.4821	−39	175	0.25	13.8	5.8	−3.6	12.9
BN Eri	....	−29	163	0.25	13.55	5.1	−2.5	12.9
BG Eri	0.6599	−32	173	0.25	13.75	5.6	−3.0	13.0
BP Eri	....	−32	172	0.25	13.8	5.8	−3.0	13.2
AI Tau	0.5686	−25	137	0.8	13.7	5.5	−2.3	13.4
HV 10416 *	....	−28	175	0.25	13.9	6.0	−2.8	13.5
WY Eri	0.5069	−42	173	0.25	14.1	6.6	−4.4	13.6
HV 7665	....	+19	141	0.7	13.75	5.6	+1.8	13.7
AG Eri	0.5125	−38	178	0.25	14.45	7.8	−4.8	14.6
XX Eri	0.7102	−42	171	0.25	14.5	7.9	−5.3	14.8
CK Tau	....	−23	156	0.8	14.2	6.9	−2.7	14.9
AE Eri	0.6214	−39	177	0.25	14.6	8.3	−5.2	15.1
AB Eri	0.5740	−41	180	0.25	14.85	9.3	−6.1	15.9
GO Ori	....	−21	161	0.25	14.55	8.1	−2.9	16.0
HV 6284	....	−40	178	0.25	14.9	9.6	−6.1	16.2
AI Eri	0.6195	−39	179	0.25	15.0	10.0	−6.3	16.6
AP Eri	0.4211	−37	180	0.25	15.05	10.2	−6.2	16.8
AD Eri	0.4699	−40	178	0.25	15.1	10.5	−6.7	17.1
HV 10402	....	−30	165	0.25	14.95	9.8	−4.9	17.2
HV 7655 *	....	+16.5	138	1.05	14.85:	9.3:	+2.6:	17.5:
BO Eri	....	−29	166	0.25	15.05	10.2	−5.0	17.7
HV 10396	....	−23	160	0.25	15.05	10.2	−4.0	18.0
YZ Eri	0.3574	−43	179	0.25	15.5	12.6	−8.6	18.8
FV Ori	0.5522	−24	162	0.25	15.65	13.5	−5.5	21.1

* Not certainly classified as a cluster type cepheid.

a true indication of the galactic extent can be derived from this material.

The cluster type variables are listed in Table 13 in order of increasing distance from the center of the galaxy.[1] The tabulated quantities, except for the period of variation (given only when accurately known), have been identified in the formulae above. It is at once evident that these stars must be members of the corona of our galactic system, described below, and not members of the relatively thin galactic discoid. Their distances z from the galactic plane require that conclusion.

The low-latitude obscuring clouds have so far prevented us from measuring the total extent of the galactic discoid in the anti-center direction. We have as yet little evidence that the discoid can be traced out to more than a few kiloparsecs with variable stars in Taurus and Auriga, although some of the fainter classical cepheids in Monoceros, as well as those in Cygnus, suggest that such discoid-inhabiting objects are seen at great distances from us and from the galactic center. The radio telescopes may eventually take over the discoid tracing.

B. The extent of the stellar corona

Although we have not yet found in the anti-center region any discoid members at large distances, we have shown for this anti-center octant the great extent of the stellar corona. Its radius is considerably more than the fifteen kiloparsecs that we have in recent years commonly accepted for the radius of the galactic system. For thirteen stars of Table 13, $d_g > 15$ kpc; eleven are farther from the sun than the sun is from the galactic center. Many are more than five kiloparsecs above or below the galactic plane—clearly lying far outside the galactic discoid.

If the cluster variables may be taken to provide a fair indication of the nature of the general population in the stellar corona, we must conclude that the stellar density is very low at the farthest distances here explored. The population falls off rapidly with distance. The contribution of the surrounding corona to the total galactic mass must now be quite negligible, although, because of its location, it may be

1. Harlow Shapley and Ann B. Hearn, *Proc. Nat. Acad. Sci.*, *38*, 839–43 (1952) (Harv. Reprint 367).

significant in galactic dynamics. In the early history of our galaxy, according to current plausible theory, the coronal population was much richer and the fall-off with distance from the galactic plane not so marked as now. A similar decrease of population density with distance from the galactic plane in the direction of the south galactic pole is summarized in a later section of this chapter.

C. Diameter of the galactic discoid

On the basis of our present surveys of the galactic boundaries, which are supplemented by work with radio telescopes, we can take seven kiloparsecs as the extent of the discoid beyond the sun in the anti-center direction. This value indicates a total radius of the discoidal system, with its several spiral arms, as fifteen kiloparsecs. Naturally we assume a considerable degree of symmetry for our Sb spiral and propose, therefore, as the total diameter of the galactic system in its equatorial plane, not including the corona, a value of 30 kiloparsecs, or, in round numbers, 100,000 light years. The central oblate spheroid, the galactic nucleus, has an equatorial diameter of about one-fifth of the whole. The central "bulge" therefore begins to appear at about two-thirds of the distance in from the sun to the center.

D. The thickness of our Galaxy

The thickness of the discoid of our spiral varies from a few hundred parsecs near its outer edges to two or three thousand parsecs at the center. The boundaries are indefinite, of course, and the foregoing numbers have little meaning except to indicate that the thickness increases from edge to center.

The dimensions of the surrounding stellar corona are also indefinite, and the best we can do is to record the distances at which we find objects that appear certainly to be members of our galactic system. These scattered stars, mostly in high latitudes, are sometimes considered as escapes from the highly massive nucleus and from "crowded" discoidal regions; or, alternatively, as remnants of an original spherical system most of whose stars have now been "pulled down" into the discoid where dust and gas contribute to the control. An earlier suggestion that the distant cluster type cepheids in high latitudes are stars that have escaped from globular star clusters, where such variables are sometimes very common, is no longer seriously held because of the wide distribution of these high-latitude cluster variables and their considerable number. The coronal stars may, of course, include both the ejected "escapes" and the "remnants" of an originally spheroidal galaxy.

Most of the distant cluster type variables that are now on record were found through studies of the Harvard photographs, although Baade [2] found some remote variables of this type in his early Bergedorf studies of globular clusters, as did also S. I. Bailey and Ida Woods at Harvard. A dozen Harvard observers have now added much to the increasing number. The detection of these variables in high latitudes is slow work because of their relative scarcity. Without abundant plate material and clear evidence from color values, an eclipsing star of the W Ursae Majoris type can occasionally be confused with cluster type variables.

The ten cluster variables now on record as the most distant from the galactic plane in the southern galactic hemisphere are the following:

	Galactic		
Name	Latitude	$\dot{m}_o$	z in kpc
HV 6426	−84	16.15	15.1
RZ Scl	−77	15.5	10.9
RY Phe	−62	15.7	10.9
HV 6242	−38	16.45	10.7
HV 6395	−63	15.6	10.5
HV 6373	−62	15.6	10.4
AW Aqr	−58	15.6	10.0
SX Scl	−82	15.25	9.9
HV 6372	−66	15.35	9.6
AR Aqr	−56	15.55	9.5

In northern galactic latitudes several variables with $z > 12$ kpc are known. The over-all thickness of the corona, and of our Galaxy, may therefore be put as greater than 25 kpc, or roughly 80,000 light years.

A check on the thickness of the Galaxy is provided by the high-latitude globular clusters. Omitting four remote newly discovered clusters for which distances are not yet available, we have the follow-

2. *Ast. Nach.*, *244*, 153 (1931).

ing tabulation of the five clusters most distant on the north of the galactic plane and the five most distant on the south:

NGC	β	$r \sin \beta$ in kpc	NGC	β	$r \sin \beta$ in kpc
5634	+48°	+24	7492	−64°	−23
6229	+40	+19	7006	−21	−16
4147	+79	+19.6	6864	−27	−19
5024	+79	+19.8	1261	−51	−17
5053	+78	+17.0	288	−88	−14.5
	Mean	+19.3		Mean	−17.5

The separation of the means is 36.8 kpc, indicating a diameter of the coronal spheroid that encompasses these far-flung globular clusters of more than 120,000 light years.

E. The galactic concentration of coronal cepheids

The available data on the occurrence and magnitudes of cluster type cepheids in high latitudes indicated as early as 1930, with greater certainty than had theretofore been attained,[3] that an extensive low-density "atmosphere" or "stellar corona" exists as an integral part of the galactic system. A similar corona or halo has been shown for Messier 31 by the photoelectric work of Stebbins and Whitford,[4] and by microdensitometer measures on Harvard and Michigan photographs.[5] Its extent and density are not yet well determined.

On the basis of a discussion of about 180 selected cepheids in high southern galactic latitudes we derive below a value of the galactic concentration of cluster type variables. This is, in a sense, a determination of the frequency of these stars as a function of distance from the galactic plane. When the observational material is much enriched this density gradient may have considerable importance in studies of the dynamics of the galactic system. A summary of the method and conclusions follows.

3. *Proc. Nat. Acad. Sci.*, 25, 423–8 (1939) (Harv. Reprint 173). See also Harv. Reprints 81 (1933) and 118 (1936).

4. Joel Stebbins and Albert E. Whitford, *Proc. Nat. Acad. Sci.*, 20, 93–8 (1934).

5. *Mon. Not. Roy. Ast. Soc.*, 94, 791–816 (1934) (Harv. Reprint 105); see also Robley C. Williams and W. Albert Hiltner, *Mich. Publ.*, 8, 103–6 (1943).

About 3,000 cluster type cepheids outside globular clusters are now known, but many of them have not been worked up and published. Probably several thousand remain undiscovered in the galactic nucleus and elsewhere. There are, however, the few hundred in high galactic latitude that are sufficiently well known to serve in the derivation of at least a provisional density gradient. But a meaningful result can be obtained for any chosen group of fields only if we have a search so thorough that practically all variables are discovered.

For a considerable number of high-latitude fields the series of plates examined at Harvard has been sufficient to make the search for the cluster type variable stars practically complete to the magnitude limit reached with the 10-inch Metcalf triplet at Bloemfontain when exposures of 45 minutes are made on Cramer Hi-Speed plates. Fortunately the shortness of the periods and the continuous variation of these stars make such completeness of discovery possible without the extended series of plates that would be required to provide definitive periods and light curves, or that would be necessary for the discovery and study of Algol stars. Nor do we need for this work a long time interval, such as would be appropriate for long-period variables.

Table 14. Fields Thoroughly Searched

VSF	Longitude	Latitude	Variables
202	45°	−20°	13
204	135	−20	3
209	0	−40	32
211	170	−40	13
212	270	−40	25
213	0	−60	15
214	95	−60	7
215	180	−60	7
216	270	−60	13
217	180	−80	8
218	356	−80	9
259	240	−30	15
344	251	−27.5	7
566	245	−46	13

Table 14 contains a list of fourteen fields in the southern galactic hemisphere, with latitudes not less than 20°, in which the search for cluster type cepheids is accepted as complete. Each field effectively covers 80 square degrees, but for the two fields centered on β −20°

only the higher-latitude half is used in the present work. In VSF 209 there are more than five times as many cluster variables per unit area as in VSF 204; nevertheless the number per field is in general fairly uniform since only three out of fourteen fields have less than seven or more than fifteen cluster variables. The total area surveyed, over 1,000 square degrees, may be considered a sufficient sample to give a preliminary value of the population characteristics in the stellar corona. On the average there is one cluster variable in every 6 square degrees.

In Table 15 the number of variables is given for equal intervals of distance from the galactic plane, and in the last column, the logarithms of these numbers when reduced to unit volume of space. In computing the distances of the variables from the median apparent magnitudes $\dot{m}$, a total photographic space absorption of 0.25 magnitude has been adopted; that is, the corrected distance d_c in parsecs, is given by

$$d_c = 10^{0.2(\dot{m}+4.75)}.$$

For these high latitudes a mean value of the space absorption appears appropriate; as does also the assumption implied in the equation that the absorption lies wholly this side of the variables. The essential transparency in the direction of these particular fields is assured by the counts of faint external galaxies shown on the long-exposure

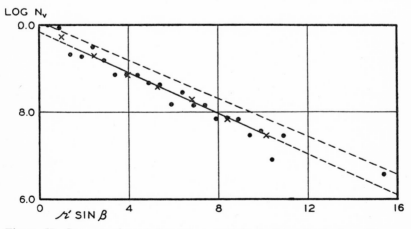

Figure 57. Concentration of cluster-type cepheids to the galactic plane. Crosses indicate means. The broken line represents Equation (7); for it the observations are not plotted.

plates. Incidentally, globular clusters are not found in any of the fields listed, and the variables discussed here are therefore presumably quite independent of the clusters.

Table 15. Frequency of Cluster Variables in South Galactic Hemisphere

Interval of Distance from Galactic Plane (kpc)	Number of Variables Observed	Mean Distance from Plane (kpc)	Log Number Reduced to Unit Volume
0.0– 0.5	1	0.48	0.0
0.5– 1.0	6	0.84	9.93
1.0– 1.5	4	1.22	9.32
1.5– 2.0	7	1.78	9.28
2.0– 2.5	19	2.30	9.49
2.5– 3.0	14	2.69	9.19
3.0– 3.5	9	3.18	8.85
3.5– 4.0	12	3.72	8.85
4.0– 4.5	15	4.25	8.84
4.5– 5.0	13	4.73	8.68
5.0– 5.5	14	5.24	8.63
5.5– 6.0	6	5.76	8.18
6.0– 6.5	13	6.18	8.44
6.5– 7.0	8	6.82	8.16
7.0– 7.5	9	7.20	8.15
7.5– 8.0	5	7.75	7.84
8.0– 8.5	6	8.20	7.87
8.5– 9.0	6	8.72	7.81
9.0– 9.5	3	9.22	7.47
9.5–10.0	4	9.74	7.54
10.0–10.5	1	10.4	6.90
10.5–11.0	4	10.76	7.46
15.0–15.5	1	15.06	6.56

The concentration of cluster variables toward the galactic plane is shown graphically in Figure 57 based on columns 1 and 4 of Table 15. (Perhaps the same gradient holds for whatever other stars there may be in these outer regions.) To the accuracy permitted by the observations, the density function, shown by table and graph, may be written as a linear relation between the distance from the galactic plane, $d_c \sin \beta$, and the logarithm of the number of cluster variables per unit volume of space:

$$\log N_v = -0.15 - 0.235 d_c \sin \beta \qquad (6)$$

If we consider only the ten fields (142 variables in 800 square degrees) with latitudes from $-40°$ to $-90°$, the relation becomes

$$\log N_v = 0.09 - 0.22 d_c \sin \beta \qquad (7)$$

when the data are reduced to the same unit volume as that used in equation (6). This second relation is probably to be preferred for two reasons: the space-absorption correction is more dependable for the higher latitudes (for example, VSF 202 in β $-20°$ is probably infiltered by the Taurus nebulosity), and the four fields with lowest latitude may be less completely surveyed than supposed, since the number of variables per unit volume is disproportionately small.

In general, the entries at the beginning and end of Table 15 and the corresponding plotted points are of low weight because of the small numbers involved; also for magnitudes corresponding to $d_c \sin \beta > 10$ kpc uncertainty arises from the approach to the plate limit. The plotted crosses in Figure 57 are means of three. The broken line represents equation (7).

The unit of volume used in Table 15 is 0.065 cubic kiloparsecs, computed from the sufficiently approximate relation

$$V_i = 0.0010 \sum_1^{14} csc^3 \beta_i,$$

where the limits refer to the fields in Table 14 (MWF 202 and 204 are half fields) and the coefficient is the volume in cubic kiloparsecs of a cone of solid angle 80 square degrees and height 0.5 kpc.

From equation (6) for the population function, it appears that at the galactic plane, where

$$d_c \sin \beta = 0$$

and therefore

$$N_v = 0.71,$$

there are eleven cluster variables per cubic parsec. At a distance of ten kiloparsecs from the galactic plane this number has dropped to 0.05. Although the *rate* of decrease is fairly well determined, the space density is not.

If equation (7) is used, we have $N_v = 1.23$ at the galactic plane; consequently we have 19 variables per cubic parsec for $d_c \sin \beta = 0$, and 0.12 for $d_c \sin \beta = 10$ kpc.

The foregoing calculations refer to the high-latitude sky as observed from our position, 8.2 kpc from the galactic center. The gradient would probably be quite different if determined by an observer in the central spheroid. The number of completed high-latitude fields in the northern galactic hemisphere is as yet too small to give a dependable determination of the galactic concentration on that side of the plane; presumably it does not differ significantly from that on the south.

F. Nonvariable stars in the galactic polar zones

Whether the remote high-latitude cluster type variables are remnants or runaways, we naturally expect nonvariable stars also to exist in the galactic corona. Such appears to be the fact. Small color indices for some 10th magnitude stars showed up in early Harvard work on colors and spectra in the north galactic zone, presumably indicating high luminosity and great distances; but the major and most convincing proof of a coronal population of nonvariable stars came in 1946 in the photometric and spectroscopic work at Palomar and Mount Wilson by Humason and Zwicky.[6] In the region of the north galactic pole they found 31 blue stars, with apparent magnitudes 10 to 15, of which 28 have normal "early type" spectra and therefore have absolute magnitudes so bright that the stars must be far outside the galactic discoid. Luyten and Carpenter have supplemented this work with a magnitude, color, and proper-motion program in 45 Selected Areas.[7] In the first report on their survey they record 35 blue stars far from the galactic plane, and assign them to membership in the galactic corona. A few superluminous classical cepheids and most of the globular clusters help to establish the corona of our Galaxy as a tempting region for further research.

There is indeed much yet to be learned about the stellar population in the polar zones—about the variables, normal stars, and nearby white dwarfs. We need to know more of the stellar motions in those regions, and the presence of dark and bright nebulosity, however thin. The relative abundance of the cluster type variables at distances still greater than heretofore explored should be investigated, since

6. M. L. Humason and F. Zwicky, *Astroph. Jour., 105*, 85 (1947) (*Mt. Wilson Contr.*, No. 724).

7. Willem J. Luyten and Edwin F. Carpenter, *Ast. Jour., 60*, 429 (1955).

that would lead to the intriguing question of the existence of wandering intergalactic stars.

Since our Galaxy, at least in appearance, is typical of a large class of spirals, the details here presented on its dimensions and its stellar corona have seemed appropriate for a treatise on the Inner Metagalaxy. But in the final chapter we shall again turn our attention from local affairs to the orientation of galaxies in space, and to their erratic grouping, and conclude with some speculations on their evolution.

CHAPTER 14. MISCELLANY ON ORIENTATION, INTERGALACTIC ABSORPTION, EVOLUTION

I. ORIENTATION IN SPACE OF FLATTENED GALAXIES

The writer has for years maintained a sympathetic but skeptical interest in the study of orientation of the central planes of galaxies. The images of a large majority of the objects entering our general surveys are elongated. Precisely spheroidal galaxies are rare. But most of the images are so slightly elongated that accurate measures of the position angles of the longest axes, or of the ratios of minor to major axes, are not possible. A random catalogue of a hundred or so faint galaxies will, however, show a score or more that are accurately measurable. For them we ask: Are the position angles of the major axes distributed at random or is there a preferential direction? And in any such group is there a preferential ratio of minor to major axes? Are the planes of the galaxies in the Inner Metagalaxy preferentially parallel or perpendicular to our galactic plane?

My skepticism with respect to these questions arises from the knowledge that in all our surveys we have as yet covered much less than 1 per cent of galaxy-populated space. A measurable parallelism of galactic planes, or some other systematic arrangement that has some cosmic meaning, seems unlikely. Certainly we can hardly expect our Galaxy, or any other giant galaxy, to control gravitationally the orientation in space of the central planes of distant galaxies, or expect the position of our galactic plane to be controlled or even appreciably affected by our neighbors. That there are vestiges of some "original" generalized orientation is the best we could propose, and such a proposition is both vague and without clear reason.

Nevertheless, improbable as it may seem, there is growing evidence of deviation from randomicity in the orientation of galactic planes.

A. On preferential orientations

For some thirty-five years the question of the orientation of galactic planes has been the intimate concern of F. G. Brown.[1] With J. R. Reynolds he has examined the position angles of the major axes of the elongated images of bright galaxies, and using Harvard estimates of elongation and position angles for faint galaxies in Horologium [2] he has found evidence of systematic arrangements sufficient to justify serious consideration of a phenomenon which, if securely proved to be existent, must be of high importance in the history of the Metagalaxy.

The most thorough examination of the question is an investigation by Wyatt and Brown of a nebular region in Cetus.[3] They have also summarized all previous work in this field and looked into the relevant material in other Harvard catalogues of faint galaxies (e.g., those of Adelaide Ames and R. H. Baker). The new measures refer to 800 galaxies photographed in 28 centers with the 24–36-inch Curtis-Schmidt telescope of the University of Michigan. Wyatt and Brown find that the highly flattened galaxies are "overabundant" for the assumption of a random orientation of galactic planes. In summary they state:

The frequency function of position angle differs markedly from a constant function, with a peak at 130°. The probability that such a skew sample can be drawn from a parent population whose rotation vectors are distributed in random directions is only about 10^{-5}. Within the limitations of the survey, the observed frequeny function is independent of (a) location within the area examined, (b) projected shape of the galaxies, and (c) angular size of the galaxies.

The frequency function of the projected shape also deviates notably from the curve expected on the basis of random distribution of rotation axes, in the sense that there is a considerable preponderance of edge-on galaxies. It is shown, however, that this result may be due to a selection effect in surface brightness that operates in favor of systems seen edgewise. Unlike the results from position angles, it is not possible to assert

1. *Mon. Not. Roy. Ast. Soc., 81*, 129 (1920); *82*, 510 (1922); *98*, 218 (1938); *99*, 14, 534 (1939).

2. *Harv. Ann., 88*, No. 5 (1935).

3. S. P. Wyatt, Jr., and F. G. Brown, *Ast. Jour., 60*, 415–22 (1955).

whether galaxy inclinations to the line of sight are distributed preferentially or at random in the Cetus area.

Wyatt and Brown found for the 710 measurably elongated images that the number of galaxies with position angles of the major axes at 120° to 130° was almost double the number for other position angles.

Since the work is to be extended to other fields, nothing more need be said here about these new results, except to repeat that if a systematic preferential orientation of galactic planes is uncovered, even for a small fraction of 1 per cent of explorable space, it will be of high significance in metagalactic dynamics.

II. A TEST FOR HIGH-LATITUDE ABSORPTION

The most conspicuous unevenness in the distribution of galaxies in latitudes between +30° and —30° is commonly attributed to dust clouds inside our own Galaxy. In these low latitudes the presence of effective absorption is shown also in the distribution of stars. For example, the absorption is faintly shown in the distribution of stars as well as galaxies around the north celestial pole,[4] but more emphatically in the Cygnus to Sagittarius rift in the Milky Way where both galaxies and distant stars are completely blotted out.

B. *Evidence of transparency*

The question arises whether or not the unevenness in the distribution of high-latitude galaxies is also due to clouds of absorbing material, either near the galactic plane or farther out, possibly in the intergalactic regions. And if it is caused by nonuniform intervening light scattering, will the high-latitude galactic stars also show an analogous uneven distribution? They should if the absorption is interstellar near the galactic plane. Extragalactic absorption of sufficient density seems very unlikely. It must, however, be kept in mind as a possible contributing factor.

A test for the possible correlation of stellar with nebular distribution is provided in Table 16 and in Figures 58 and 59 for eight fields

4. Cf. Chapter 7, Sec. II, above.

in the north galactic zone. On each plate the numbers of stars and galaxies were counted in two contrasting square degrees, one rich in number of galaxies and one relatively poor. The square degrees chosen in each plate are adjacent; on one plate two pairs of squares were counted. Only areas close enough to the plate centers to be free of appreciable distance correction were used. The star counts by Mr. Forbes (F) include for each pair all stars brighter than a selected faint magnitude that was alike for rich and poor fields, but usually different from the limits selected by Miss Hearn (H).

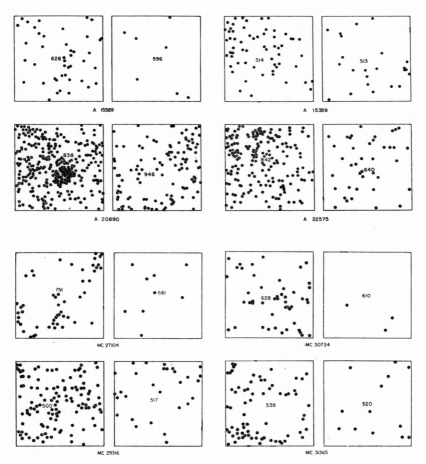

Figures 58 and 59. The distribution of galaxies (dots) and stars (numbers) in four pairs of high-latitude fields

The areas examined on plate A 22575 show what may be a significant excess of stars in the galaxy-rich square, but it may be that the excess on this plate arises in part from our identifying as stars a number of the fainter spheroidal galaxies.

In the diagrams, the actual positions of the recognized galaxies are plotted; and the mean star count for each square degree is recorded by a number. In the last double column of Table 16 are the ratios of

Table 16. Distribution of Galaxies

Plate No. (Mag. Limit)	Galactic Coordinates Rich	Poor	Number of Galaxies Rich	Poor	Number of Stars Rich	Poor	Ratios Galaxies	Stars
A 15389	λ 248°	244°	43	7	F 512	464	6.1	1.05
(18.1)	β +69	+69			H 740	727		
	254	250	62	23	F 481	486	2.7	1.00
	+68	+69			H 546	540		
A 20890	264	265	320	116	F 795	922	2.8	0.89
(18.6)	+68	+70			H 882	971		
A 22575	204	210	186	40	F 734	512	4.6	1.32
(18.4)	+73	+72			H 950	768		
MC 27104	106	100	51	9	F 732	644	5.7	1.14
(18.4)	+64	+63			H 770	678		
MC 29316	185	191	118	29	F 460	526	4.1	0.97
(18.1)	+80	+79			F 493	515		
					H 548	511		
MC 30734	75	83	48	3	F 631	607	16.0	1.03
(18.0)	+80	+79.5			H 625	614		
MC 31365	166	168	72	13	F 419	483	5.5	1.04
(18.0)	+84	+85			F 577	558		
					H 620	519		

rich fields to poor for galaxies and for stars. They clearly show that the foreground stellar distribution is essentially smooth in these high latitudes and is independent of the nebular fluctuations.

If our conclusion is correct that the uneven distribution of galaxies in high latitudes reflects not uneven space absorption (in our Galaxy or outside) but merely the nonhomogeneous structure of the Metagalaxy, we should be able to diminish the observed large differences between rich and poor in galaxy counts by extending the census in the affected regions to the 20th magnitude. The test of using fainter objects should also be applied to the star counts for plate A 22575 before the recorded results for star numbers are accepted as indicating a localized absorption of two- or three-tenths of a magnitude, spread over the star-poor region on that plate.

The present examination [5] for fields in latitudes greater than $\pm 60°$ confirms the similar test [6] in 1932 for eight pairs of fields with latitudes between $\pm 26°$ and $\pm 53°$ and one pair at $-70°$. The irregular distribution of galaxies in high latitudes has been reported many times in the course of the Harvard surveys. The apparent clustering has also been analyzed by Bok,[7] and more recently by Shane [8] and his collaborators on the basis of photographs made with the Carnegie Astrograph at the Lick Observatory.

III. ON THE EVOLUTION OF GALAXIES

Commonly in the astronomical literature we find the terms "early type galaxy" and "late type galaxy." They suggest that a progression prevails in form and presumably in the age or stage of development. The galaxy series runs from the spheroidal systems, E0, like Messier 87 and Messier 60, through forms of increasing flattening, E1 to E7, to the compact spirals, S0 and Sa, and the open spirals, Sb, Sc, Sd— eventually perhaps to the irregular galaxies like the Magellanic Clouds and *IC* 1613. Assuming an evolution through the forms in the direction E0 to Sd, we have the concept of young to old, or "early" to "late."

A basis for this terminology lies in the assumption that the spheroidal forms are smaller than the spirals, and the further assumption that they grow centrifugally, E0 to E7 to Sd, through rotation. It was formerly assumed also that the spiral arms are ejections of material (stars and gas) from the central nuclei—a result likewise attributed to increasingly rapid rotation. But certainly the argument based on relative dimensions, and probably the ejection hypothesis, should be abandoned.

5. Cf. *Pub. Ast. Soc. Pac.*, *65*, 237–41 (1953).
6. *Harv. Bul.*, No. 890 (1932).
7. Bart J. Bok, *Harv. Bul.*, No. 895 (1934).
8. C. D. Shane and C. A. Wirtanen, *Proc. Am. Phil. Soc.*, *94*, 13–17 (1950); J. Neyman, E. L. Scott, and C. D. Shane, *Astroph. Jour.*, *117*, 92 (1953).

C. Comparative sizes of galaxies

We can easily dispose of the illusion that the spheroidals are relatively small compared with the spirals by tabulating the early Mount Wilson estimates of the diameters of bright galaxies along with the much more revealing microphotometer measures of diameters of these same objects as shown on Harvard long-exposure photographs. In Table 17 the galaxy class is that assigned by Hubble.[9] The magnitudes are

Table 17. Diameters of Galaxies

			Diameter		
NGC	Type	Magnitude	Mt. W.	Dens.	Dens./Mt. W.
4472	E	10.1	2.'0	16.'3	8.2
4486	E	10.7	2.0	11.5	5.8
4570	E	12.0	2.4	6.0	2.5
4636	E	10.8	1.2	6.9	5.7
4649	E	10.6	2.0	10.2	5.1
4371	SBa	12.1	1.5	6.2	4.1
4429	Sa	11.7	3.0	9.9	3.3
4442	SBa	11.4	3.2	7.4	2.3
4526	Sa	10.7	5.0	10.8	2.2
4643	SBa	11.6	1.8	4.6	2.6
4665	Sa	11.8	1.2	4.6	3.8
2976	Sc	11.2	3.2	7.6	2.4
4517	Sc	11.6	10.0	11.9	1.2
4536	Sc	11.2	7.1	5.4	0.8
4579	SBc	11.0	2.8	10.3	3.7
4632	Sc	12.1	3.2	4.2	1.3
4666	Sc	11.3	4.0	6.0	1.5
3034	I	9.4	7.0	14.0	2.0
3077	I	11.4	3.0	10.4	3.5

from the Shapley-Ames catalogue, and their rather narrow spread suggests that we are dealing with fairly homogeneous material. All but three of the spirals and spheroidals are in the Virgo assemblage.

9. *Astroph. Jour., 64,* 321–69 (1926) (*Mt. Wilson Contr.,* No. 324). It should be noted that Hubble (*Astroph. Jour., 71,* 231–76 (1930) (*Mt. Wilson Contr.,* No. 398) and Carroll and Moss (*Mon. Not. Roy. Ast. Soc., 91,* 199 (1930)) also found that densitometer measures extend the diameters, especially for some of the spheroidal galaxies, over those obtained by visual inspection of the photographs.

Hubble's diameters in the fourth column are followed in the fifth by the densitometric measures, and in the last column by the ratios of the two. The densitometer measures show a large increase for all types. The diameters of the spheroidals are increased by 5.4 times on the average, but the spirals by only 2.3 times. From the tabulation of diameters we have in the mean:

Galaxy class	E (5)	Sa (6)	Sc (6)	I (2)
Mt. Wilson estimates	1′.9	2′.6	5′.0	5′.0
Densitometer	10′.2	7′.2	7′.6	12′.5
Mean of ratios	5.4	3.0	1.8	2.8

Additional work on diameters confirms this preliminary evidence that the spheroidal and spiral types are of comparable linear extent.[10]

D. The direction of development

Theoretical investigations of the masses, temperatures, and luminosities of stars, and of the evolution of condensing dust clouds, lead to the hypothesis that the stars in the spiral arms have recently—in the last hundred million years—condensed out of the residual dust and gas of a rotating galaxy. Supergiant stars, it is believed, are currently emerging. As yet there is no evidence of material such as protostars shooting out of the nuclei; rather, a spiral's new stars "precipitate" out of the aggregated star stuff in the region where they are now found.

There can be little question but that the spirals, and presumably all galaxies except possibly the truly spheroidal systems, are in rotation. Except near the center of a galaxy, the rotational speed, angular and linear, decreases with distance from the gravitational center. In consequence, shearing action arises to tear aggregations apart. B. J. Bok has examined quantitatively this problem in celestial dynamics [11] and finds that loose clusters will in the course of a galactic revolution or two become streams of stars and eventually disappear as physical entities. In the same way the star clouds of a spiral arm must be dismembered, because of the differential rotational speeds, and gradually absorbed into the amorphous star fields of the discoid. The evolution

10. *Darwin Lecture, Mon. Not. Roy. Ast. Soc.,* 94, 791–816 (1934) (Harv. Reprint 105).

11. Bart J. Bok, *Mon. Not. Roy. Ast. Soc.,* 106, 63–5 (1946) (Harv. Reprint 284).

is toward smoothness of structure. Von Weizsäcker has pointed to the turbulence in star clouds, which must also tend to smooth out irregularities. The direction of the development of a spiral galaxy, therefore, should on this alternative hypothesis be toward the smooth-structured classes, that is, from Sd and Sc toward Sb and Sa, and on to the oblate spheroids. In other words, the direction is opposite to that formerly assumed, and the terms "early" and "late" could well be reversed.[12] But rotational flattening may also be involved in the development of the spheroids, as with globular clusters where some elongated forms are detected (ω Centauri, Messier 19, and Messier 62).[13] A spiral's tendency to disrupt and smooth out its star clouds and open clusters, and to burn out its young supergiant stars, may not mean that a galaxy like ours will go all the way to sphericity.

On the suggested scheme of development, the Magellanic Clouds should evolve in the direction of smoother organizations, the Large Cloud probably to become a regular barred spiral, the Small Cloud a dwarfish spheroidal, like the Sculptor supercluster mentioned in Chapter 9. The Small Cloud, however, may skip the spiral stages, which appear to be reserved for the more massive galaxies. (Cf. Chap. 4, § J.)

An inquiry by Reaves into the fainter galaxies of the Virgo cluster suggests that dwarfs of about the same size and luminosity as the smallest of the local group may be as abundant in that organization as the largest galaxies.[14] He finds 48 of the special type of *IC* 3475—a type not represented among those assigned to our local group. The Sculptor and irregular dwarf types could not be clearly identified on the plates made with the Lick Observatory's Carnegie Astrograph, but Reaves reports that A. G. Wilson with the Palomar 48-inch Schmidt telescope has picked out numerous faint objects in the Virgo cluster that he considers to be probable Sculptor-like galaxies. This work supports the conclusion from inspection of the luminosities of the local group in Table 10 that the luminosity function for galaxies is very asymmetric, far from the Maxwellian distribution function formerly assumed. The most common galaxy is small compared with

12. *Pub. Obs. Mich., 10,* 82 (1951) (Harv. Reprint, Ser. II, 37).
13. For the clusters, however, passage through galactic star fields might be the source of deformation.
14. Gibson Reaves, *Ast. Jour., 61,* 69–76 (1956).

our galactic system; its star population is in the millions rather than in the billions. The future of its structure, like that of a globular cluster, is an open speculation.

The evolution of galaxies that we have been considering is based on variety in form from type to type. Guillermo Haro has called attention in a personal letter to the variety that exists in the spectrum of the nuclei of spirals. A given form, Sb for example, can show large differences in the integrated colors of the nucleus. Its bright spectral lines may be strong, weak, or wholly absent. Perhaps we shall need eventually a complete two-dimensional classification—morphological and astrophysical—and a two-way evolutional scheme.

In conclusion, we should observe that the development or evolution of a galaxy is an inevitable result of its stars shining away their masses and of its varied speeds of rotation dissolving its loose clusters and star clouds. Mighty operations are going on. We should not, however, be too confident that this is a one-way process. The supergiant stars quickly run through their energy stores, and star groups dissolve into the amorphous background. But apparently new stars in new configurations currently emerge in the irregular and spiral galaxies that are rich in interstellar dust and gas. Such raw material, unevenly distributed, exists between the stars and in intergalactic space; it may be replenished and maintained through supernova activity or otherwise. When conditions are right it will be swept up by stars or into evolving proto-stars.

Galaxies can therefore grow in mass by accretion while they decay through radiation, and the two processes may be more nearly in balance than now is believed.

APPENDICES

The Distribution of Magnitudes for 22 Plates

	]15.0	15.0	15.1	15.2	15.3	15.4	15.5	15.6	15.7	15.8	15.9	16.0	16.1	16.2	16.3	16.4	16.5	16.6	16.7	16.8
A 20280	4	1	0	0	4	1	3	1	2	4	2	4	1	2	4	1	4	2	3	7
20318	4	0	0	0	2	3	3	1	2	4	0	3	3	3	3	7	3	8	12	14
17182	0	0	1	1	0	1	0	0	0	0	1	0	0	1	0	0	1	2	3	4
15781	4	0	0	3	1	5	0	2	1	1	2	2	2	2	1	0	4	5	5	8
17777	1	0	0	1	0	2	0	2	1	0	1	0	2	1	1	2	0	5	3	3
20484	3	0	1	1	2	0	1	1	1	3	2	3	1	4	3	4	8	5	4	4
20341	13	2	2	3	0	2	1	3	1	5	2	4	3	3	4	4	10	4	11	10
19788	6	3	1	0	1	2	0	2	1	8	3	2	3	4	3	4	7	4	4	3
20347	2	1	2	2	1	0	1	3	1	8	4	3	6	5	7	15	23	15	22	25
17867	5	5	1	2	1	3	2	0	2	7	2	3	3	0	8	4	4	4	6	6
20503	10	1	0	0	2	0	3	1	3	2	1	1	0	1	0	3	6	4	7	6
17084	7	0	3	2	3	2	0	1	0	2	2	3	4	10	8	3	6	9	5	9
16253	13	2	2	0	4	0	1	3	3	5	5	3	7	4	6	6	6	18	10	15
18691	2	0	4	2	3	2	1	2	2	1	5	6	14	10	9	16	9	11	4	11
16213	2	0	2	0	3	3	2	0	0	1	2	3	0	2	2	5	2	6	2	9
18706	7	2	2	2	0	1	3	0	1	6	2	8	9	3	12	8	9	6	13	17
18809	1	0	1	0	0	0	0	1	0	0	1	0	0	1	2	5	0	7	3	4
15814	3	0	0	1	1	1	1	0	0	0	1	0	1	4	4	4	6	3	5	6
20440	1	1	0	0	2	1	0	3	3	0	7	3	2	7	7	10	15	8	14	16
17946	4	2	1	0	2	0	0	1	2	2	4	2	9	4	7	9	11	9	10	10
20433	17	5	2	4	2	3	1	2	0	5	2	4	3	9	4	8	11	12	10	20
17971	15	1	2	4	1	2	1	5	2	6	5	5	6	3	4	8	9	9	14	4
22 Plates	124	26	27	27	32	34	24	34	28	60	56	62	79	83	99	126	154	156	170	211
13 "	75	15	18	16	19	18	14	22	17	39	34	33	46	42	51	75	91	90	95	106
5 "	26	6	8	9	7	9	5	10	8	17	15	17	26	18	25	34	30	34	31	28

	16.9	17.0	17.1	17.2	17.3	17.4	17.5	17.6	17.7	17.8	17.9	18.0	18.1	18.2	18.3	18.4	18.5	18.6	18.7	[18.7
A 20280	10	19	18	30	21	22	23	30	35	28	25	12	15	6	2					
20318	16	33	19	36	30	27	42	45	74	69	81	66	62	38	16					
17182	4	5	4	8	4	7	12	13	11	20	24	23	21	20	34	29	29	11	1	
15781	6	13	15	30	21	30	27	10	14	6	10	3								
17777	4	14	8	6	17	13	23	18	21	34	43	36	28	47	37	57	66	32	8	
20484	4	11	11	10	20	20	16	20	16	21	26	31	21	44	52	71	74	46	51	125
20341	15	13	10	24	20	29	35	42	46	61	45	35	43	51	63	62	72	43	15	
19788	2	6	7	11	16	21	27	36	42	46	54	61	43	19	3					
20347	19	16	22	27	25	31	48	56	48	60	82	77	103	101	84	38	5			
17867	5	3	8	11	13	10	16	15	18	25	29	31	18	29	28	40	37	60	80	226
20503	9	12	13	14	27	37	33	32	34	44	39	49	35	42	41	40	48	49	32	5
17084	10	10	8	19	19	21	17	21	31	21	21	12	8	9	2					
16253	20	19	23	22	23	26	28	26	30	38	42	49	67	27	19	14	2			
18691	13	11	11	28	21	19	22	35	37	39	30	43	54	66	98	83	101	106	115	295
16213	5	5	4	10	10	8	13	10	21	14	31	31	30	32	16	6	1			
18706	26	15	18	23	26	28	24	32	26	16	17	14	10	2	3					
18809	7	8	13	7	10	17	20	30	22	28	29	13								
15814	1	4	10	11	4	11	9	11	17	42	42	43	32	14	7					
20440	19	15	31	41	51	58	58	69	71	72	65	52	46	28	16	4				
17946	9	10	21	46	45	48	51	63	105	115	106	79	42	10						
20433	16	25	23	21	21	30	39	69	85	94	123	108	79	41	7					
17971	8	11	13	24	38	25	43	34	33	30	51	37	37	49	34	54	79	84	80	81
22 Plates	228	278	310	459	482	538	626	717	837	923	1015	905	794	675	562	498	514	431	382	732
13 "	109	130	144	206	238	257	325	348	374	474	538	546	532	541	516	494	514	431	382	732
5 "	34	50	51	79	109	87	120	122	125	149	179	178	158	235	249	305	357	328	334	727

Appendix B (see Chapter 6). Galaxies in the North Galactic Zone

Plate Number	Galactic Long.	Lat.	N_9	m_s	$\bar{N}_r$
A 6718	245°	+73°	285	17.8	36.4
6719	258	+80	366	17.8	46.8
6720	262	+75	204	17.9	22.7
13810	255	+70	521	17.9	57.9
14551	232	+77	423	17.9	47.0
14699	257	+64	173	17.9	19.2
15251	251	+64	95	17.1	31.9
15363	280	+80	88	17.1	29.6
15370	278	+74	125	17.6	21.0
15384	296	+73	158	17.7	23.3
15389	249	+69	278	18.1	23.4
16086	263	+60	411	17.5	79.5
16090	344	+62	241	17.9	26.8
16407	341	+69	347	18.0	33.6
16757	324	+59	231	17.8	29.6
17345	267	+65	726	18.0	70.3
17468	194	+66	329	17.5	63.6
17721	335	+74	500	17.9	55.6
17761	298	+70	1,168	18.2	85.7
17774	328	+60	362	18.3	23.1
18291	313	+60	604	18.4	33.6
18296	311	+68	503	18.5	24.5
18391	255	+59	441	18.2	32.3
18489	189	+62	312	18.0	30.2
18506	336	+64	538	18.6	22.7
19063	212	+60	424	17.9	47.2
19349	218	+78	862	17.8	110.1
19422	320	+71	670	18.4	37.2
19522	286	+72	876	18.0	84.8
19986	294	+65	668	18.3	42.7
19990	321	+78	540	18.0	52.2
20095	304	+63	618	18.2	45.4
20107	210	+67	628	18.1	53.0
20115	351	+62	387	17.6	64.9
20117	220	+71	673	17.6	112.9
20670	281	+66	657	18.4	36.4
20705	226	+60	548	18.3	35.0
20862	198	+70	918	18.4	51.0
20880	219	+64	582	18.1	49.2
20890	269	+70	1,635	18.6	69.0
20918	276	+65	1,092	18.8	34.9

Plate Number	Galactic Long.	Lat.	N_9	m_s	$\bar{N}_r$
A 20922	268°	+60°	796	18.6	33.6
21719	241	+62	658	18.3	42.0
21926	320	+64	1,766	18.6	74.5
22393	296	+81	1,435	18.5	69.7
22464	203	+63	882	18.3	56.2
22569	227	+67	834	18.7	30.6
22575	206	+74	944	18.4	52.4
23089	296	+63	278	18.4	15.4
23153	280	+64	418	18.4	23.2
24821	306	+74	240	18.2	17.6
24823	327	+68	861	18.0	83.0
26301	285	+62	488	18.5	23.7
26304	332	+57	548	18.5	26.7
26704	230	+74	1,712	18.8	54.8
26848	340	+58	622	18.4	34.6
26857	238	+70	430	18.0	41.6
MC 27104	105	+65	336	18.4	23.6
27134	16	+87	838	18.5	51.2
27599	111	+84	277	18.1	29.6
27639	115	+72	371	18.3	30.1
27641	108	+62	614	18.5	37.6
27688	95	+59	262	17.9	36.7
27704	98	+74	206	18.1	22.0
28719	106	+57	319	18.1	34.0
28754	115	+67	339	17.8	64.3
28788	129	+68	216	18.1	23.0
28868	120	+58	185	18.3	15.0
28914	63	+59	194	17.8	31.2
28938	100	+69	279	18.0	34.1
29265	142	+58	420	18.4	29.4
29283	137	+64	273	18.5	16.7
29316	198	+80	568	18.1	60.6
29377	70	+68	161	17.8	25.9
29382	185	+69	279	18.1	29.8
29447	58	+64	179	17.9	25.1
29494	40	+70	357	17.7	66.2
29498	73	+57	283	17.8	45.6
29526	303	+85	283	18.0	34.6
29530	354	+69	437	17.9	61.2
29532	341	+80	454	18.1	48.4
29606	52	+59	163	17.8	26.2
29612	32	+65	304	17.3	98.0
29945	149	+61	288	18.3	23.3

Appendix B (Continued)

Plate Number	Galactic Long.	Lat.	N_0	m_s	$\bar{N}_r$
MC 29949	138°	+71°	251	18.0	30.7
29962	47	+65	233	18.3	18.9
29978	146	+66	306	18.0	37.4
29979	41	+61	142	18.1	15.1
29981	27	+74	464	17.8	74.8
29986	124	+76	390	17.8	62.9
29987	31	+59	268	17.7	49.8
29988	158	+62	186	17.8	30.0
29989	22	+68	198	17.5	48.4
30038	74	+74	447	18.0	54.7
30041	83	+59	210	17.7	39.0
30045	170	+62	170	17.8	27.3
30129	55	+70	329	18.1	35.1
30734	73	+79	288	18.0	35.2
30740	131	+58	612	18.1	65.3
30797	97	+64	366	17.8	59.0
30837	72	+63	169	17.6	35.9
30851	85	+64	394	17.8	63.4
30879	102	+79	145	18.0	17.8
31292	125	+63	192	17.6	40.8
31358	230	+85	124	17.7	23.0
31359	85	+69	212	17.8	34.1
31365	158	+86	344	18.0	42.0
31368	60	+83	124	17.7	23.0
31431	166	+81	299	17.5	73.1
31432	142	+79	360	17.7	66.8
31440	10	+80	176	17.9	24.6
31442	35	+79	413	17.7	76.7
31444	50	+75	214	17.5	52.3
32130	154	+74	411	17.6	87.2
32148	174	+76	196	17.5	47.9
32157	159	+66	224	17.6	47.6
32226	358	+65	471	17.9	65.9
32281	9	+68	173	17.6	36.7
32284	191	+75	277	17.4	77.6
32867	172	+68	564	17.8	90.9
32872	180	+63	497	17.7	92.2
32908	350	+75	462	17.8	74.4
32914	10	+63	363	17.9	50.8
33347	7	+75	542	18.0	66.2
33360	244	+81	166	18.0	20.3
33924	20	+62	250	17.4	70.0

Appendix C (see Chapter 7). Summary of the Census in the
South Celestial Polar Zone (Plates in Order of Right Ascension)

Plate	λ	β	N_{tot}	$\bar{N}_9$	$m_{n(s)}$
A 14232	273°1	−50°3	383	8.7	18.4
17219	274.1	−55.0	896	13.9	18.3
17198	268.5	−40.2	411	6.1	18.1
17088	264.2	−54.9	465	10.4	18.0
17222	264.0	−49.7	1,106	18.6	18.5
17121	255.2	−53.0	461	14.6	17.7
17144	256.3	−47.6	362	5.8	17.9
17150	257.3	−45.0	384	12.3	17.6
14395	261.0	−40.9	263	7.8	18.0
14265	247.7	−49.4	834	18.1	17.9
16344	263.1	−36.3	432	12.2	17.7
17155	250.4	−43.8	533	9.8	17.9
17097	244.6	−46.7	756	28.4	17.2
17200	266.3	−31.5	278	4.7	18.0
17163	253.0	−38.2	1,923	48.3	17.6
16350	240.0	−40.5	745	41.9	17.3
17187	243.0	−38.6	3,018	59.0	17.6
16686	254.3	−34.4	1,170	27.2	17.6
16732	238.9	−37.0	2,361	60.9	17.5
16641	238.8	−30.3	347	15.4	17.1
16315	255.9	−29.4	195	5.1	17.7
17193	261.8	−28.8	195	8.2	17.3
16368	250.1	−27.9	462	15.2	17.5
16758	244.6	−26.2	1,292	18.6	18.0
14256	239.6	−25.3	458	18.1	17.4
17211	264.5	−27.6	340	10.2	17.6
17256	251.2	−23.5	548	11.3	17.5
17312	241.2	−19.6	453	10.2	17.8
17250	246.8	−20.2	562	10.6	17.7
17351	244.1	−14.5	283	7.1	17.8
14626	253.0	−19.4	42	2.5	(17.5)
17398	258.0	−21.5	459	3.2	18.6
17391	249.9	−15.3	676	16.4	17.8
16696	247.8	−10.1	150	5.0	17.6
16075	257.4	−14.9	64	1.7	(17.3)
16919	252.1	− 6.0	66	0.9	(17.7)
16316	261.6	−18.2	104	1.2	17.8
16330	257.1	− 9.0	79	3.9	(17.6)
16934	256.6	− 3.3	98	6.6	17.1
16366	262.7	−11.7	192	7.5	17.4
16481	261.3	+ 1.2	84	6.2	(17.2)
16950	267.8	−20.4	270	3.9	17.7

Appendix C (Continued)

Plate	λ	β	N_{tot}	$\bar{N}_9$	$m_{n(s)}$
A 16406	264°6	— 6°3	22	1.3	(17.5)
16073	264.6	— 1.0	81	2.4	17.3
16011	267.6	—16.0	78	0.3	17.8
16134	268.1	— 5.3	47	4.1	(17.5)
14529	270.8	— 0.3	66	2.4	17.4
16033	271.6	—10.6	107	3.3	(18.0)
16452	271.3	—15.5	140	2.8	17.7
14996	270.0	—27.7	326	15.3	17.2
16450	275.8	— 6.2	81	3.3	(17.4)
16418	278.3	— 1.7	83	3.0	17.4
17405	271.5	—25.9	278	2.0	18.1
16439	284.3	— 4.3	41	0.6	(17.9)
17401	274.5	—21.6	361	1.0	18.6
16414	277.5	—17.6	136	2.3	18.1
16167	283.0	— 8.9	34	1.2	(17.8)
16169	280.5	—13.3	82	3.8	(18.0)
16120	290.0	— 8.4	50	1.1	(17.7)
14845	285.1	—17.1	38	1.9	(17.7)
16185	289.0	—14.0	106	3.6	(18.0)
16195	295.1	—13.4	224	9.1	17.7
16525	291.1	—16.6	41	1.2	(17.4)
14862	282.4	—22.7	96	4.0	(18.3)
16218	298.4	—19.3	249	16.6	17.1
17473	278.1	—26.3	51	0.9	(18.0)
14184	283.6	—24.9	261	6.6	17.9
14202	294.6	—23.8	67	2.3	(18.9)
14208	289.2	—25.5	73	2.7	(19.0)
14222	300.6	—25.8	514	14.3	18.2
14267	295.4	—31.6	208	3.6	17.7
18629	283.9	—31.4	469	7.3	18.1
14229	304.5	—33.5	351	7.7	18.3
16945	275.2	—29.5	1,544	9.2	17.9
14239	289.0	—34.0	325	4.0	18.1
16961	277.2	—31.7	472	6.6	17.8
14293	293.4	—38.6	436	8.3	18.0
17087	299.0	—41.7	381	5.0	18.4
14325	285.7	—39.4	555	12.7	17.9
14251	280.0	—37.4	130	4.1	17.4
14329	293.5	—48.9	535	11.4	17.9
14219	286.9	—45.9	872	13.4	17.9
14213	283.8	—47.6	517	7.2	17.8
16299	280.0	—43.9	308	4.4	18.5
14268	285.0	—53.0	474	7.4	18.0
16976	272.4	—35.0	624	9.1	17.8
17194	272.8	—40.0	497	8.1	17.7

Appendix D (see Chapter 7). Summary of the Census in the North
Celestial Polar Zone (Plates in Order of Right Ascension)

Plate	λ	β	N_{tot}	$\bar{N}_{25}$	$m_{n(s)}$
MC 27801	89°6	+25°4	112	5.8	17.1:
28009	92.4	+10.5	21	0.5	(18.0)
27997	92.9	+15.7	21	0.4	(18.1)
28001	92.6	+21.5	141	3.7	(18.0)
26932	97.8	+11.9	53	1.0	17.6:
27990	97.4	+17.9	74	1.8	(18.2)
28166	102.3	+15.0	47	1.3	(18.0)
28034	95.9	+23.6	105	3.3	17.4
28048	100.9	+20.3	173	4.1	17.6
28595b	105.7	+18.4	379	9.1	17.7
28054	103.0	+24.9	308	10.0	17.4
27640	108.6	+23.4	588	12.2	17.5
28049	98.8	+27.1	411	10.4	17.6
28089	93.2	+28.2	136	6.3	17.3
27521	109.8	+28.7	491	9.7	17.7
28666	104.7	+29.7	431	6.4	17.9
26903	109.0	+34.1	605	13.4	17.6
28261	97.7	+31.2	234	7.0	17.4
28667	102.3	+34.9	540	11.2	17.8
28239	106.1	+39.0	482	12.1	17.6
28161	97.9	+38.1	518	19.8	17.3
28056	101.7	+42.3	699	23.6	17.3
28078	93.8	+35.0	333	9.1	17.4
28057	90.5	+30.4	224	5.6	17.6
28086	92.8	+40.3	314	11.8	17.3
28095	93.0	+44.7	568	20.0	17.4
27635	89.5	+35.3	555	18.0	17.3
27194	86.6	+45.7	558	12.8	17.7
27645	86.9	+40.3	973	27.0	17.5
28158	79.2	+42.7	354	11.6	17.3
28172	81.5	+37.9	425	15.2	17.4
27088	86.1	+32.6	511	14.2	17.5
27373	75.1	+39.9	386	10.8	17.5
27462	75.9	+37.1	399	9.7	17.6
27192	79.9	+34.3	623	15.4	17.6
27273	87.9	+29.4	274	11.8	(17.5)
27230	70.5	+35.2	770	14.6	17.8
27279	75.7	+29.6	605	17.0	17.5
27288	70.0	+29.5	548	15.5	17.5
27445	82.6	+28.8	447	8.2	17.5

Appendix D (Continued)

Plate	λ	β	N_{tot}	$\bar{N}_{25}$	$m_{n(s)}$
MC 28478	70°.5	+24°.2	330	13.8	17.2
27293	76.7	+24.8	225	6.2	17.6:
27753	82.0	+25.9	255	4.9	17.7
27832	73.7	+19.6	32	0.9	(17.8)
27796	79.6	+20.2	62	2.4	(17.7)
27833	76.8	+15.4	34	1.3	(17.8)
27808	84.8	+22.0	61	2.2	(17.8)
27836	82.8	+17.7	38	1.4	(17.8)
29121	80.8	+12.1	20	0.6	(18.1)
27866	87.3	+15.6	35	0.9	(18.1)
26807	86.6	+10.0	50	0.4	17.7
27837	88.5	+20.5	61	2.5	(17.8)

Appendix E (see Chapter 7). Positions and Counts of Galaxies in the Canopy (Plates in Order of Right Ascension)

λ	β	m_s	$\bar{N}_r$	λ	β	m_s	$\bar{N}_r$	λ	β	m_s	$\bar{N}_r$
90°	+25°	17.6	5.7	102°	+35°	18.2	11.8	94°	+54°	17.8	41.7
93	22	18.0	4.2	145	47	18.4	13.2	95	59	17.9	30.3
96	24	17.8	3.7	124	45	17.8	13.1	98	74	18.1	20.6
101	20	18.2	3.7					91	50	17.8	31.3
112	21	18.0	5.3	138	47	17.9	34.0	85	69	17.8	27.0
103	25	17.9	9.7	112	41	17.6	18.9	90	35	18.1	13.6
109	23	18.1	7.9	106	39	18.1	11.7	85	64	17.8	55.5
99	27	18.0	11.6	129	49	17.7	34.8				
130	20	18.5	3.8	144	52	18.5	18.0	74	74	18.0	40.8
125	22	18.3	2.9	116	46	18.0	17.1	83	59	17.7	32.7
				134	53	18.0	26.6	87	46	18.1	13.6
120	24	18.1	11.2	120	50	18.2	21.6	83	55	17.6	23.9
115	26	18.2	10.2	126	54	17.9	42.8	87	40	18.0	28.9
136	23	18.2	17.0	142	58	18.4	21.9	70	68	17.8	20.2
93	28	17.7	6.5					83	50	17.8	26.7
131	24	18.0	10.3	107	45	17.7	26.8	72	63	17.6	29.6
141	23	18.3	10.7	131	58	18.1	54.5	55	70	18.1	27.1
110	29	18.2	10.4	98	38	17.9	18.1	73	57	17.8	40.9
126	27	18.2	13.3	111	50	17.6	19.5				
121	30	18.1	13.0	102	42	17.9	22.3	75	53	17.6	31.7
105	30	18.3	7.9	115	54	17.9	26.0	58	64	17.9	22.8
				137	64	18.5	14.2	63	59	17.8	26.0
115	31	18.1	7.9	120	58	18.3	14.7	47	65	18.3	13.4
138	29	18.0	16.6	94	35	17.9	10.6	77	47	17.6	33.5
143	29	18.2	11.9	125	63	17.6	34.7	79	43	17.7	15.7
133	32	18.4	14.4					52	59	17.8	26.1
127	33	17.7	32.2	99	44	17.9	23.2	64	53	17.4	35.2
138	35	17.9	19.1	129	68	18.1	18.1	41	61	18.1	14.4
121	35	18.0	23.4	100	49	17.7	24.5	68	49	17.4	46.6
145	35	18.0	20.3	103	53	17.7	42.2				
109	34	18.5	8.8	106	57	18.1	31.5	82	38	17.7	19.1
133	36	17.9	23.7	115	67	17.8	49.3	56	55	17.5	39.0
				108	62	18.5	32.1	86	33	17.8	18.9
98	31	18.1	5.5	90	30	18.0	5.6	37	56	18.0	14.4
126	39	17.8	14.7	115	72	18.3	22.4	45	54	17.5	29.9
144	40	18.2	18.9	93	40	17.6	15.6	60	49	17.5	23.5
114	37	17.7	27.8					71	44	17.5	43.3
138	41	18.1	30.8	93	45	17.7	24.8	75	40	17.9	12.5
132	43	17.8	27.0	100	69	18.0	27.7	51	50	18.0	23.4
119	41	17.8	13.4	97	64	17.8	49.0	42	49	18.1	20.3

Appendix E (Continued)

λ	β	m_s	$\bar{N}_r$	λ	β	m_s	$\bar{N}_r$	λ	β	m_s	$\bar{N}_r$
63°	+44°	18.0	17.0	41°	+37°	17.7	21.2	49°	+26°	17.7	8.4
36	49	18.2	37.6	65	34	17.5	25.4	39	20	18.0	6.6
76	37	17.8	12.9	59	33	17.8	12.5	45	20	17.3	8.5
56	44	17.5	29.2	36	32	18.3	14.1	50	21	17.3	14.4
80	34	17.9	18.8	53	33	17.9	16.6	55	21	17.7	9.8
88	29	17.5	15.5					60	22	17.8	12.9
49	44	17.6	29.0	47	32	17.8	18.4	70	24	17.8	13.1
67	38	17.8	32.8	42	31	17.6	22.3	66	23	18.1	7.7
42	43	17.6	19.3	76	30	17.8	23.2	77	25	18.0	6.4
35	43	18.0	32.7	38	26	17.7	19.7	82	26	18.2	5.5
				70	29	17.8	20.2				
60	39	17.3	43.5	83	29	18.2	9.4	80	20	17.7	2.5
71	35	18.2	17.4	59	29	17.5	18.1	85	22	17.8	2.4
53	38	17.5	24.9	43	25	17.6	7.9	89	20	17.8	2.3
47	38	17.7	24.6	65	29	17.7	12.5				
35	38	17.9	14.7	54	27	17.9	15.2				

SUBJECT INDEX

Absorption: at North Pole, 106 ff.; in anti-center octant, 164; in high latitudes, 178–81

Andromeda Nebula, vi, 20, 80, 118

Anti-center of galactic system, 16, 153, 162–6

Beyond the galactic center, 148, 149

Bruce classification of galaxies, 17, 18

Canopy of galaxies, 15, 24, 109–14

Celestial smog, 93

Census of galaxy population: south galactic polar zone, 188, 189; north galactic polar zone, 190 ff.; south celestial polar zone, 193, 194; north celestial polar zone, 195, 196; Canopy, 197, 198

Centaurus cloud of galaxies, 125

Centaurus window, 16, 149

Center of Milky Way: 39, 154–61; its direction, 154–9; its distance, 159–61; as indicated by globular clusters, 154–60; by cepheid-galaxy method, 161

Cepheid-galaxy method: of measuring distance to galactic center, 161; of measuring space absorption, 144, 151, 152, 161–7

Cluster cepheids: of the anti-center, 162–7; in high latitudes, 167–8

Clusters, globular: vi; in locating galactic center, 154–60

Clusters of galaxies: 96, 97, 125–9; in Fornax, 125; Lick Observatory maps, 133, 135, 137; photometry of 25 clusters, 128, 129; two large metagalactic clusters, 129; in Virgo, 22, 26, 33, 34, 38, 68, 87, 92, 126, 127, 184

Wolf's "Nebelneste" (Coma cluster), 125, 127, 128, Fig. 43

Wolf's Perseus cluster, 125, 128

Coma cluster of galaxies, 125, 127, 128, Fig. 43

Constellations in Magellanic Clouds, 53, 54

Corona of galactic system, extent of, 166–74

Coverage of eleven surveys, 7–19

Declination $+43°$ belt, 10, 14, 15, 122 ff.

Densitometer dimensions of galaxies, 183

Density gradients, 14, 81–4, 100, 115, 132–5

Diameter of galactic system, 162–75

Direction of galaxy evolution, 183–5

Double galaxies, v

Dwarf galaxies of general field, 130 ff.

Eclipsing binaries, 39, 147

Evolution: of galaxies, 181–5; of Magellanic Clouds, 47, 64, 65, 181, 184

Fornax group of galaxies, vii, 26, 34

Fornax supercluster (galaxy), vi, vii, 22, 23, 47, 68

Frequency of galaxy types, 20, 21, 35 ff., 130, 131

Galactic concentration of coronal cepheids, 169–74

Galactic systems, diameters of, 162–75

Galaxies:
a billion within reach, 114
angular dimensions, 26, 27, 30, 182, 183
associated, and doubles, v
Bruce classification, 17, 18
clusters of, 22, 26, 33 ff., 38, 68, 87, 92, 96, 97, 125–9, 133, 135, 184
comparative sizes, 182, 183
diameters measured with micro-densitometer, 30
distribution of brightest, 28 ff.
Dreyer catalogues, 24, 96
dwarf irregular, 24

NAME INDEX